INTERSCIENCE TRACTS ON PHYSICS AND ASTRONOMY

Edited by R. E. Marshak

University of Rochester

Additional volumes in preparation

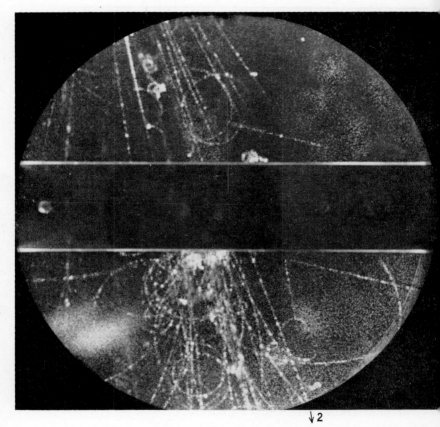

↓2

First cloud chamber photograph of a neutral V-particle. Obtained by G. D. Rochester and C. C. Butler at the University of Manchester, the V-particle was produced in a 3-inch thick lead plate and decayed into two particles identified by the arrows labeled 1 and 2 at the edge of the figure. (Reproduced through the courtesy of *Nature*.)

STRANGE PARTICLES

ROBERT KEMP ADAIR

Professor of Physics, Yale University
New Haven, Connecticut

EARLE CABELL FOWLER

Professor of Physics, Duke University
Durham, North Carolina

1963
INTERSCIENCE PUBLISHERS
a division of John Wiley & Sons, New York • London

Scarcely more than a decade ago it appeared to many of us that the study of the physics of elementary particles was entering a period of refinement and consolidation. The paths of study of the weak interactions seemed well determined, the pi-meson appeared to have all of the qualities necessary to account for the strong interactions, essential simplicities seemed to be established, and the two V-tracks in the chamber of Rochester and Butler covered an area no larger than a man's hand.

Now after more than ten years progress we see again that God is more subtle than we would suppose. Our simplicities were but the shadows of a more complex reality. The V-particles were a particular indication of this complexity, an indication of another dimension of the elementary particles themselves—the dimension we now call strangeness.

It is the purpose of this work to summarize the important properties of the strange particles in the context of basic, or at least popular, theoretical ideas. Particular emphasis has been placed on the analysis and interpretation of important experimental results. An attempt has been made to introduce some insight into the physical basis of many formal results by the use of models, analogies, and the correspondence principle. Chapter 5 contains a concise collection of results, not always conveniently available, which are useful in the interpretation of experimental results.

Such a monograph is necessarily limited in subject matter and in time. Therefore, we ask of the reader some familiarity with the physics of pions and nucleons, and a recognition that

very quickly some of the discussion will concern only history—
things as they were and not as they are.

   It is a pleasure to take this opportunity to thank our secretary,
Miss Joanne Izzo, for the many hours which she has devoted to
the preparation of this manuscript. We also wish to thank Mrs.
Joan Blum of John Wiley and Sons for her patient help in
turning our manuscript into a printed tract.

Yale University
New Haven, Connecticut   ROBERT K. ADAIR
November, 1962   EARLE C. FOWLER

Contents

CHAPTER 1

Introduction

1.1. Early History[1]

The earliest identification of an example of what we now call strange particles was reported by L. Le Prince-Ringuet[2] in 1944. A secondary cosmic-ray particle crossing his cloud chamber struck an electron, transferring considerable momentum to the electron at a measurable angle. From measurement of the curvature of the tracks produced by the magnetic field, and application of conservation of energy and momentum, the mass of this particle was found to be 500 ± 50 Mev/c^2. The particle was undoubtedly a K-meson, but the implication of this single observation at a time prior to the discovery of the pion was not clear.

In 1947, G. D. Rochester and C. C. Butler at the University of Manchester arranged a magnetic cloud chamber containing a 3-inch thick lead plate to be triggered by an array of Geiger-Muller counters which selected showers of penetrating cosmic-ray particles in the vicinity of their chamber. After about a year of operation near sea level, they reported[3] two examples of the decay in flight of a new type of particle, called, phenomonologically, from their appearance in the cloud chamber, V-particles (frontispiece). They presented a number of possible explanations of these two events without invoking the idea of new particles. However, evaluation of these alternatives left them with the conclusion that the most likely explanation was in terms of the decay of new particles with lifetime between 10^{-9} and 10^{-11} seconds.

1

The study of elementary particles and their interactions as they could be observed in the secondary cosmic radiation reached its peak in the years between 1946 and 1954. Studies of the properties of elementary particles had long been vigorously pursued, and the discovery of the charged pion,[4] the long-sought Yukawa particle, by C. F. Powell and his collaborators in 1946–1947 accelerated the search. Rochester and Butler's discovery was followed by increased emphasis on high altitude exposure of similar experimental arrangements. The elaborate character of a magnetic cloud chamber and its auxiliary equipment limited these experiments to ground-based altitudes, but gains in counting rate of an order of magnitude for the penetrating shower detectors over that achieved at sea level were obtained at places ranging from Mount Palomar to the slopes of Mont Blanc. The new V-particles were investigated intensively by cloud chamber groups from various institutions for several years.[5] Even under the best conditions, the collection of V-particles of any particular type was a slow process. By the time of the Bagnères Conference[6] in July 1953, however, essential facts about V-particles had been determined, not only by the cloud chamber work, but also by thorough investigation by nuclear emulsion techniques. In the cosmic-ray studies, which are nearly always characterized by a great variety of events, the precision and reliability of certain types of emulsion measurements, particularly those involving ranges and the identification of stopped particles through grain density and multiple scattering measurements, resulted in the preeminence of emulsion work in the studies of stopped particles. With some notable exceptions, most of the early knowledge of the charged K-mesons came from these studies.[7]

It is not possible here to mention all or even most of the early experimental results; however, before summarizing the situation at the time of the Bagnères Conference, which marks the transition from "natural" to "man-made" strange particles, we should like to mention two cosmic-ray studies which exemplify the more drastic turning points.

First, there had been a great amount of seemingly conflicting data about neutral V's until a new level of accuracy in momentum and angle measurement in cloud chambers was attained by R. W. Thompson.[5c] His experiments established definitely the distinction between the V_1^0 which was the phenomenological representation of the decay $\Lambda^0 \rightarrow p + \pi^-$ and V_2^0 which represented the decay $\theta^0 \rightarrow \pi^+ + \pi^-$. These are not the only decay modes of these particles as can be seen in Table 2-1. This work not only established the identity of the θ^0, but it was not until these particles were available in large numbers at the bevatron that a more accurate determination of the θ^0 mass was made.

Second, there had been speculation concerning the existence of a charged counterpart of the θ^0. The $\tau^+ \rightarrow \pi^+ + \pi^- + \pi^+$ had been established in the early work with emulsions and the mass of the θ^0 was about the same as the τ. Other three-particle decays of positive particles with approximately this mass (now called $K_{\mu 3}$ and $K_{\pi 3}$) had been identified in emulsion studies. In this early work the probability of identifying a K-meson decaying to two pions in emulsion was reduced because of the higher energy of the secondaries. Many investigators believed that Rossi and his collaborators[5e] had established that some of the charged V's and the M. I. T. S-particles, so named because they stopped in plates of a cloud chamber, included such particles. In that climate, a single event from the Princeton group seemed to silence further speculation on this matter. They reported[8] a positively charged particle which decayed into a π^+-meson and two e^+-e^- pairs (internally converted) establishing $\theta^+ \rightarrow \pi^+ + \pi^0$ as nearly as it could be in one picture.

The facts which seemed well-established by cosmic ray investigations by the end of 1953 were as follows[6]:

1. Some V-particles decay in modes which yield protons and pions, and are, therefore, heavier than the proton.

2. Some V-particles are lighter than the proton and can decay to yield pions. Some also yield muons, electrons, and probably neutrinos.

3. Lifetimes vary over the entire interval readily observable with cloud chambers, from 10^{-8} down to 10^{-10} seconds.

4. A collision between two particles which interact with the strength of the nuclear force is reasonably likely to yield V-particles (it may be as small as 1/100 the chance of producing π^- mesons in a penetrating shower, but the V-particle production is not thousands of times less than π-production).

5. There exists at least one type of V-particle which can decay into another V-particle.

The currently accepted nomenclature for the elementary particles was first established by members of the Bagnères Conference. Present rules may be summarized as follows (see Table 2-1):

1. The nucleons and heavier particles which decay to nucleons are called *baryons*.

2. The heavier strange baryons are called *hyperons* and labelled generically Y.

3. The pion and particles with mass intermediate between the pion and the baryons are called *mesons*.

4. The heavier strange mesons are labelled generically *K-mesons*.

5. Because of the fact that the μ-meson or muon does not interact strongly with nucleons, it is classified as a *lepton*, along with the electron and the neutrino.

6. As definite identifications are made for new particles, they are to be designated by Greek letters; capitals for hyperons and lower case for mesons, respectively. In normal usage the generic label may override this rule; e. g., K-mesons.

The more or less frequent production of the V-particles in nuclear collisions as compared to pion production would seem to be inconsistent with the decay rates to protons and/or pions by many orders of magnitude. The principle of microscopic reversibility states that a reaction must proceed at the same rate in either direction except for factors which depend on the spins of the particles and on the available phase space. One of the most common V-particles (Λ^0) was neutral and decayed $V_1{}^0 \rightarrow p + \pi^-$; $t_{\text{decay}} \doteq 2.5 \times 10^{-10}$ seconds. Now a typical "interaction time" or rate for a nuclear reaction is of the order of magnitude of the time for a pion having nearly the velocity of light to travel a distance equal to the range of the nuclear force, or about 10^{-23} seconds. The only thing "strange" about the V-particles is this suggestion of the violation of the principle of microscopic reversibility. Before the experimental discovery of the pion, the same argument[9] had been used to show the likelihood that the muon discovered experimentally in 1937 could not be the nuclear force meson predicted by Yukawa. The crucial fact in that argument had been the long time (about 10^{-6} seconds) which a negative muon could spend in intimate contact with a carbon nucleus without any nuclear interaction.[10] One must be reluctant to give up a postulate deeply embedded in physics which fits precisely a large body of experimental data. In this case, physicists found the explanation of apparent violation of the fundamental reversibility postulate in the existence of the pion. It is the Yukawa meson. The pion is produced copiously in nuclear interactions and interacts strongly with nuclei.

In the case of the V-particles, physicists introduced a variety of explanations, but it is Pais' hypothesis of "associated production" of V-particles which has survived.[11] This particular explanation, that only certain combinations of V-particles can be produced in association with one another when nuclear interactions occur, has been retained and made specific by the introduction of a "strangeness" quantum number for each of these "strange" particles by Gell-Mann and Nishijima.[12] Strict conservation of "strangeness" in nuclear reactions corresponds to "associated production" of V-particles. Violation of strangeness conservation in decay gives the long lifetimes observed there. Not only did the detailed study of cosmic rays lead to the identification of almost all of the strange particles, but it also stimulated the introduction of the hypothesis of associated production, which was the key to the currently accepted theory. The success of this explanation has been largely responsible for the complete acceptance of the words "strange" and "strangeness" as convenient labels. The choice is unfortunate from a general standpoint in that these particles are not more strange than any other in the usually accepted meaning of the word. This seems to be a particularly good example of the desirability of inventing new words. It is practically impossible to ignore the traditional interpretation of the words "strange" and "strangeness." The situation is reminiscent of the special meaning which chemists have assigned to the word "salt." As a counter-example, we recall that the Belgian chemist, Van Helmont, invented the word "gas," and we rather wish that someone had done the same for "strangeness."

In the spring of 1952 the cosmotron, a proton synchrotron constructed at the Brookhaven National Laboratory, achieved the acceleration of protons to energies above 1 Bev. Experiments began in the winter of 1952 to 1953 and acceleration to 3 Bev was achieved in the spring of 1954. At that time, R. P. Shutt and his collaborators exposed a high-pressure (18 atmospheres) hydrogen diffusion cloud chamber to 1.4 Bev negative pions produced in the cosmotron. One of his photographs[13] (Fig. 1-1) gave the first direct evidence of associated production. Since the beam momentum was well defined, and the reaction was required to be between a negative pion and a proton; if it were assumed that only two neutral particles emerged at the first vertex, then identification of $V_1^0 \rightarrow p + \pi^-$ (at left in Fig. 1-1) permitted calculation of the mass of the missing neutral particle. That value was quite near the value for the θ^0. This indicated that in the fundamental interaction $\pi^- + p$, two neutral V-particles had been produced simultaneously. With only one event, it was possible that the particular particle which produced the V-particle which decayed in the chamber was itself some kind of a V-particle—not a negative pion at all. It was also possible that V-particles could be produced singly with more than one additional particle in the final state so that the mass calculation assuming only one missing particle was not applicable. Finally, the incoming particle may have struck an alcohol molecule instead of a hydrogen nucleus (there was about one molecule of methyl alcohol per 800 molecules of hydrogen in the sensitive

Fig. 1-1. Production of a Λ^0 by a 1.4 Bev negative pion in a hydrogen diffusion cloud chamber. The use of hydrogen and a π^- beam with well-defined momentum permitted R. P. Shutt and his collaborators to infer that the missing neutral particle is a θ^0, implying associated production of strange particles.

region). However, the interpretation given in reaction 1 was

$$\pi^- + p \rightarrow \Lambda^0 + \theta^0 \tag{1}$$

borne out in a short time by the fact that several events which were consistent with reaction 1 were found. Furthermore, one good example in which both Λ^0 and θ^0 decayed was observed. This work as well as additional evidence, both from cosmic-ray studies and from other experiments at the cosmotron, suggested but did not establish that only associated production could occur.

Another experiment, which yielded a negative result, bears on this question. If the process $p + n \rightarrow p + \Lambda^0$ or $n + n \rightarrow \Lambda^0 + \Lambda^0$ were possible, then a beam of 460 Mev protons would have more than sufficient energy to produce Λ^0's. R. L. Garwin, using the University of Chicago synchrocyclotron showed[14] that the cross section for reactions of this kind could not be greater than about 10^{-32} cm^2, which is very much smaller than the cross section for reaction 1, found by Shutt to be about 10^{-27} cm^2.

In addition to the observation concerning associated production (Λ^0 and θ^0 occurring relatively frequently as Λ^0, θ^0, but not singly or as Λ^0, Λ^0), the early cosmotron work led to the first identification of a heavy negatively charged V-particle[15] (Σ^-). Also there was the indication of a neutral particle (Σ^0) heavier than Λ^0 in these early results.[16] The positively charged heavy particle (Σ^+) had been identified somewhat earlier by both cloud chamber[17] and emulsion[18] work. The existence of a heavier strange particle, the so-called cascade hyperon (Ξ^-) was established by Cowan [19] at about this time.

Although the $\tau^+ \rightarrow \pi^+ + \pi^- + \pi^+$ had been established for some time, a variety of K-mesons (or other modes of decay) had been identified in the cosmic ray experiments.[20] The cloud chamber work on charged V's was of particular value in verifying that there were negatively charged K-mesons with decay properties like the K$^+$. Indeed, the most confusing property of K-mesons at that time was their variety.

The most clear-cut advance in the study of the strange particles was the introduction of the Gell-Mann, Nishijima scheme of classification.[12] By this time, a great deal of work had been done, many details were known and the broad outlines were clearly established, but there was much information that had been well established experimentally and yet seemed completely uncorrelated or worse, self-contradictory. The new strangeness scheme succeeded spectacularly in correlating existing data and provided frames of reference for further advances.

1.2. Symmetry Properties and Conservation Laws

It seems probable that the interactions between elementary particles can be completely described by symmetry properties and conservation laws[21] and by dimensionless numbers representing interaction strengths. Similarly, we might expect that the elementary particles, as quanta of these interactions, may be described in terms of these same symmetry properties and interaction strengths. At the present time, however, our description of the elementary particles must also include the mass, and in some cases, the magnetic moment, although in principle these are probably derivable from interaction strengths and symmetries.

Symmetries usually result in conservation laws. In the following list of symmetry properties and conservation laws, there are conservation laws listed without an accompanying explicit symmetry. The surmise is usually made that these laws can also be expressed in terms of some similar symmetries. However, the conjectures concerning such unifications have not yet been completely explored.[22]

We are familiar with a set of "classical" conservation laws; the conservation of energy and the conservation of linear momentum. These follow from invariance under translation in time and space. The conservation of angular momentum is a consequence of invariance under rotation in space. These laws then result from the homogeneity of space, or invariance with respect to a proper Lorentz transformation; that is, a Lorentz transformation without space or time inversion.

Invariance under space inversion results in a conservation law; the conservation of parity. Let us also consider invariance under time reversal, and invariance under charge conjugation, the change of particles to antiparticles. Invariance of interactions with respect to space inversion restricts observables to those which do not differentiate between a left-handed and right-handed coordinate system. Time reversal invariance allows only observables which do not depend upon the direction of time, and invariance under charge conjugation restricts observables to those which remain unchanged when all particles are changed to antiparticles. These invariances can be demonstrated in a particularly simple way. Consider a motion picture of a fundamental process, perhaps an elementary particle interaction in the presence of electric and magnetic fields resulting from charge and current distributions in the scene. If the interactions are invariant under space inversion, it will not be possible from consideration of the projected scene to determine if the film has been reversed in the projector or projected by reflection in a mirror. If the interaction is invariant under time reversal, and if entropy is not changed in the process, it will not be possible to tell if the film is run backwards, while if the interactions are invariant under charge conjugation, it will not be possible to state whether the picture is that of our universe, or an anti-universe where every particle is replaced by its antiparticle.

These three invariances are not independent. In the framework of local field theory, invariance under a proper Lorentz transformation leads to the invariance of all interactions under combined operations CPT,[23] where C is the charge conjugation operator, changing particles to antiparticles, P, the parity or space inversion operator, changing $\bar{r}$ to $-\bar{r}$, and T is the time reversal operator, changing t to $-t$. The equality of the masses and lifetimes of particles and their antiparticles follows from this theorem.

It appears that the strong interactions and electromagnetic interactions are invariant with respect to C, P, and T separately, while the weak interactions do not conserve P or C.[24] All experimental results are consistent with the assumption that T invariance holds true for all interactions[25]; consequently, from the CPT theorem, weak interactions must be invariant under CP.[26] One could not, then, determine if the photographed scene were a scene of particles viewed normally, or a scene of antiparticles projected in a mirror.

Charge independence of an interaction implies that the interaction is independent of the magnitude of the electric charge. The existence of the charge results in the differentiation of otherwise identical particles, e. g., the neutron and proton, in a manner independent of the magnitude of the charge. This differentiation of otherwise identical particles has important consequences since the symmetrization (for bosons) or antisymmetrization (for fermions) of the wave function of several particles is affected. Such states will be split in energy in the presence of an electric field even as states with spin will be split in the presence of a magnetic field. The existence of the several charge states has an importance independent of the magnitude of the electric field or the value of the fundamental charge, even as the existence of the magnetic states has an importance independent of the strength of the magnetic field or the value of Planck's constant. Even as the total angular momentum j of the system is conserved, where $2j + 1$ is the number of states, and m the component of angular momentum in the direction of the (possibly vanishing) magnetic field is conserved, so will a constructed total isotopic spin T be conserved, where $2T + 1$ is the number of states, and a component T_3, directly related to the charge, be conserved. Even as angular momentum may not be conserved locally in the presence of a space asymmetry, as in the Stark effect, isotopic spin is not conserved by interactions such as the electromagnetic interaction which depends upon the charge, or T_3, or the third direction, explicitly. The similarities between angular momentum and isotopic spin are such that they have the same group properties and are then added and resolved in exactly the same way. It appears probable that isotopic spin is conserved by strong interactions but not by weak interactions, or, of course, by electromagnetic interactions.

Four further conservation laws complete the list of established conserved quantities: the conservation of charge, of baryons, of leptons, and of strangeness. More precisely, the conservation of baryons is the conservation of B, the number of baryons minus the number of antibaryons, and the conservation of leptons is the conservation of the number of leptons minus the number of anti-leptons. To complete these definitions it is necessary to have criteria of what constitutes a particle and antiparticle. The conservation law itself, together with experiment, serves to do this for the baryons, taking the proton, by convention, as a particle. This method is not useful for leptons, largely because they are connected with each other through reactions involving neutrinos, and the whole description lacks content unless a meaningful differentiation can be made between a neutrino and an antineutrino. Such a differentiation is provided by defining an antineutrino as the state with spin and momentum aligned, and a neutrino as the antialigned state. In the limit $v/c \rightarrow 1$, this serves as a definition of lepton and antilepton, and with this definition there is conservation of leptons. The e^- and μ^- are known to be leptons, the e^+ and μ^+ are antileptons. It appears that charge[27] and baryon number,[28] and probably lepton number[29] are conserved by all interactions.

If to each baryon and meson a number is attached which is equal to the average charge of its isotopic spin group, or $Q - T_3$, where Q is the charge of the particle and T_3 is the third component of isotopic spin; this number, which is a measure of the displacement of T_3 with respect to Q, is conserved in strong interactions. Essentially for aesthetic reasons, we define a slightly different quantity, $S = 2Q - 2T_3 - B$, where B is the baryon number, and S is the strangeness which is conserved in strong interactions (Section 2.2) and electromagnetic interactions, but not in weak interactions.

It is possible that these four conservation laws are all related to similar symmetries. The conservation of charge is required by invariance of electromagnetic interactions under a gauge transformation. Conjectures have been made that similar invariances result in the other conservation laws.[22]

REFERENCES

1. (a) One may obtain detailed accounts of the development of specific questions in this field of work since 1949 by reading the Proceedings of the Annual International Conferences on High Energy Physics (at Rochester, New York, except for two years: 1958 at the CERN Laboratory and 1959 in Kiev).

    (b) In addition, reviews which are concerned with strange particles are:

    (1) G. D. Rochester and C. C. Butler, *Repts. Progr. Phys.*, **16**, 364 (1953).

    (2) M. Gell-Mann and A. H. Rosenfeld, *Annual Review of Nuclear Science*, 7 *Annual Reviews*, *Palo Alto*, *California*, 1957.

    (3) L. B. Okun, *ibid.*, 9 (1959).

    (4) C. Dilworth, G. P. S. Occhialini, and L. Scarsi, *ibid.*, **4**, (1954).

    (5) G. Franzinetti and G. Morpurgo, *Nuovo Cimento*, *Suppl.*, **6**, 469 (1957).

    (6) R. H. Dalitz, *Repts. Progr. Phys.*, **20**, 163 (1957).

    (7) J. G. Wilson, *Progress in Cosmic Ray Physics*, 2 *North Holland, Amsterdam*, 1954.

2. L. Le Prince-Ringuet and M. Lheritier, *Compt. rend.*, **219**, 618 (1944).

3. G. D. Rochester and C. C. Butler, *Nature*, **160**, 855 (1947).

4. C. M. G. Lattes, G. P. S. Occhialini, and C. F. Powell, *Nature*, **160**, 453,486 (1947).

5. We have listed a representative paper from various centers of cloud chamber work up to about 1953. In general, references to earlier work are given in these papers:

    (a) Manchester University: J. P. Astbury, J. S. Buchanan, P. Chippindale, D. D. Millar, J. A. Newth, D. I. Page, A. Rytz, and A. B. Sahiar, *Phil. Mag.*, **44**, 242 (1953).

    (b) California Institute of Technology: R. B. Leighton, S. D. Wanlass, and C. D. Anderson, *Phys. Rev.*, **89**, 148 (1953).

    (c) University of Indiana: R. W. Thompson, A. V. Buskirk, L. R. Etter, C. J. Karzmark, and R. H. Rediker, *Phys. Rev.*, **90**, 1122 (1953).

(d) University of California: W. B. Fretter, M. M. May, and N. P. Nakada, *Phys. Rev.*, **89**, 168 (1953).

(e) Massachusetts Institute of Technology: M. Annis, H. Bridge, H. Courant, S. Olbert, and B. Rossi, *Nuovo Cimento*, **9**, 624 (1952). See also *Phys. Rev.*, **91**, 362 (1953).

6. *Report on Congress on Cosmic Ray Physics*, Bagnères-de-Bigorre, France, 1953. See also L. Le Prince-Ringuet, *Annual Reviews of Nuclear Science*, **3**, *Annual Reviews, Palo Alto, California*, 1953, p. 39.

7. Representative papers from users of the nuclear emulsion techniques are :

(a) Bristol University: R. H. Brown, U. Camerini, P. H. Fowler, H. Muirhead, C. F. Powell, and D. M. Ritson, *Nature*, **163**, 82 (1949).

(b) Dublin: C. O'Ceallaigh, *Phil. Mag.*, **42**, 1032 (1951).

(c) Tata Institute, Bombay: D. Lal, Y. Pal, and B. Peters, *Proc. Indian Acad. Sci. Sect. A*, **38**, 398 (1953).

(d) University of Rochester: J. Crussard, M. Kaplon, J. Klarmann, and J. Noon, *Phys. Rev.*, **93**, 253 (1954).

8. A. L. Hodson, J. Ballam, W. H. Arnold, D. R. Harris, R. R. Rau, G. T. Reynolds and S. B. Treiman, *Phys. Rev.*, **96**, 1089 (1954).

9. S. Sakata and T. Inoue, *Progr. Theoret. Phys. (Kyoto)*, **1**, 143 (1946); H. Bethe and R. Marshak, *Phys. Rev.*, **72**, 506 (1947).

10. M. Conversi, E. Pancini, and O. Piccioni, *Phys. Rev.*, **71**, 209 (1947).

11. A. Pais, *Phys. Rev.*, **86**, 663 (1952).

12. For summaries see:
M. Gell-Mann, *Nuovo Cimento, Suppl.*, **4**, 2,848 (1956); K. Nishijima, *Progr. Theoret. Phys. (Kyoto)*, **13**, 285 (1955).

13. W. B. Fowler, R. P. Shutt, A. M. Thorndike, and W. L. Whittemore, *Phys. Rev.*, **91**, 1287 (1953).

14. R. L. Garwin, *Phys. Rev.*, **90**, 274 (1953).

15. W. B. Fowler, R. P. Shutt, A. M. Thorndike, and W. L. Whittemore, *Phys. Rev.*, **93**, 861 (1954).

16. W. D. Walker, *Phys. Rev.*, **98**, 1407 (1955).

17. C. M. York, R. B. Leighton, and E. K. Bjornerud, *Phys. Rev.*, **90**, 167 (1953).

18. A. Bonetti, R. Levi-Setti, M. Panetti, and G. Tomasini, *Nuovo Cimento*, **10**, 1736 (1953).

19. E. W. Cowan, *Phys. Rev.*, **94**, 161 (1954).

20. See list in reference 7. Also, the so-called $K_{\mu 2} \rightarrow \mu + \nu$ was first established by B. Gregory, A. Lagarrique, L. Le Prince-Ringuet, F. Muller, and C. H. Peyrou, *Nuovo Cimento*, **11**, 292 (1954).

21. A particularly useful review is presented by G. C. Wick, *Annual Review of Nuclear Science*, **8**, *Annual Reviews, Palo Alto, California*, 1958.

22. J. J. Sakurai, in P. Morse, ed., *Annals of Physics*, 11, Academic Press, New York 1960, p. 1.
23. The *CPT* theorem or Luders-Pauli theorem, reviewed by G. Luders, *Ann. Phys.*, 2, 1 (1957).
24. The work of T. D. Lee and C. N. Yang showed that existing experimental results did not establish conservation of parity in weak interactions and suggested measurements which would test this hypothesis: *Phys. Rev.*, 104, 254 (1956). The work of C. S. Wu, E. Ambler, R. Hayward, D. Hoppes, and R. Hudson, *Phys. Rev.*, 105, 1413 (1957) and later, R. Garwin, L. Lederman, and M. Weinrich, *Phys. Rev.*, 105, 1415 (1957) then established that weak interactions were invariant under neither *P* nor *C*.
25. The experimental evidence is weak; see Reference 24, and also, M. T. Burgy, V. E. Krohn, T. B. Novey, G. R. Ringo, and V. L. Telegdi, *Phys. Rev. Letters*, 1, 324 (1958); and M. Clark, J. Robson, and R. Nathans, *Phys. Rev. Letters*, 1, 100 (1958).
26. Invariance under *CP* is emphasized and called invariance under combined parity by L. Landau, *Nucl. Phys.*, 3, 254 (1957).
27. G. Feinberg and M. Goldhaber, *Proc. Nat. Acad. Sci. U.S.*, 45, 1301 (1959).
28. G. N. Flerov, D. S. Klochkov, V. S. Skobkin, and V. V. Terentev, *Soviet Phys. "Doklady" (English Transl.)* 3, 78 (1958); G. Backenstoss, H. Frauenfelder, B. Hymans, L. Koester, and P. Marin, *Nuovo Cimento*, 16, 749 (1960).
29. See the discussion by R. E. Marshak and E. C. G. Sudarshan, *Introduction to Elementary Particle Physics*, Interscience, New York, 1961.

CHAPTER 2

Properties

2.1. Table of Elementary Particle Properties

Table 2-1 lists for the thirty particles and antiparticles the properties which can be directly measured: charge, mass, spin, and for unstable particles, lifetime and decay products.

2.2. Strangeness

Determinations of the quantum numbers associated with the strange particles generally result from analyses of particle reactions and decays. Since basic symmetries are independent of detailed dynamics of processes, it is generally possible to analyze the results of experiments concerning the determination of the spins, isotopic spins, parities and strangeness quantum numbers of particles, as well as those experiments concerning the conservation laws involved in the strong and weak interactions, without the necessity of any deep understanding of the dynamics of the particle interactions. The usual description of elementary particles recognizes the obvious multiplets of particles with nearly the same mass but different charges. The strangeness scheme[3] consists of the assignment to the strongly interacting particles of strangeness quantum numbers, S, conserved in strong interactions or electromagnetic interactions, which are related to the charge center of gravity, or average charge of the multiplet, $\bar{Q}$, according to the relation: $S = A \cdot \bar{Q} + C$, where A and C are constants: $\bar{Q}$ can be otherwise defined as $Q - T_3$, where T_3 is the third component of isotopic spin of a particle and Q is the charge. Since reactions producing various numbers of neutral pions are allowed, the strangeness number for pions must equal zero. But $\bar{Q} = 0$ for pions, therefore, C must equal zero. Further, $\bar{Q}$ for nucleons is $+1/2$ while for Λ's and Σ's it is zero; hence, the difference between nucleon and lambda or sigma and the existence of reactions such as $\pi^+ + p \rightarrow \Sigma^+ + K^+$, connecting these states, establishes the K^+ strangeness as $1/2\ A$. It is then convenient to set $A = 2$ and have the change in strangeness equal to 1.

Since conservation of baryons requires no change in the number of baryons in any reaction, the value of the constant C for the baryons is arbitrary and not connected to the value for mesons. Belief in the existence of pair production of particle and antiparticle has, as consequences, that strangeness, and the value of C must have different signs for particle and antiparticle; the K^- must then have the same strangeness as Λ's and Σ's and there must be two K^0-mesons, particle and antiparticle, of strangeness 1 and -1. Though the value of the constant C for the baryons can be set equal to any number, including zero, multiplied by the baryon number, B, it is a convention to set $C = -B$, and write for all particles: $S = 2Q - 2T_3 - B$. However, the choice $C = 0$ may have advantages from the view of expressing possible symmetries.[4] The quantum number is then called hypercharge Y, and is related to the strangeness S as $Y = S + B$.

2.3. Spin

The spins of particles can often be determined by methods which have close classical analogues. Consider, for example, the reaction, $\pi^- + p \rightarrow \Lambda^0 + K^0$, in the classical limit of large quantum numbers. Assume that the K^0 has zero spin, and in the spirit of the classical limit, that the proton has zero spin. If we consider only Λ^0 produced by the interaction in the direction of the beam, at 0 or 180°, and note that in classical or

Table 2-1

Elementary Particle Properties[a]

	Particle	Anti-particle	Spin	Mass (Mev/c^2)	Mean life (sec)	Decay modes
				photon		
Photon	γ	(γ)	1	0	stable	
				leptons		
Neutrino	ν	$\bar{\nu}$	1/2	0	stable	
Electron	e^-	e^+	1/2	0.510976 ± 0.000007	stable	
Muon	μ^-	μ^+	1/2	105.655 ± 0.010	$(2.212 \pm 0.001) \times 10^{-6}$	$e^- + \nu + \bar{\nu}$
				mesons		
Pion	π^0	(π^0)	0	135.00 ± 0.05	$(2.2 \pm 0.8) \times 10^{-16}$	2γ
	π^+	π^-	0	139.59 ± 0.05	$(2.55 \pm 0.03) \times 10^{-8}$	$\mu^+ + \nu$; $e^+ + \nu$
K-meson	K^+	K^-	0	493.9 ± 0.2	$(1.224 \pm 0.013) \times 10^{-8}$	$\mu^+ + \nu$ (64.2±1.3%) $\mu^+ + \nu + \pi^0$ (4.8±0.6%) $e^+ + \nu + \pi^0$ (5.0±0.5%) $\pi^+ + \pi^0$ (18.6±0.9%) $2\pi^+ + \pi^-$ (5.7±0.3%) $\pi^+ + 2\pi^0$ (1.7±0.2%)
	K^0	$\bar{K}^0$	0	497.8 ± 0.6	K_1^0 $(1.00 \pm 0.038) \times 10^{-10}$	$\pi^+ + \pi^-$; $2\pi^0$
					K_2^0 $(6.1 \pm 1.3) \times 10^{-8}$	$\mu^+ + \nu + \pi^-$; $\mu^- + \bar{\nu} + \pi^+$ $e^+ + \nu + \pi^-$; $e^- + \bar{\nu} + \pi^+$ $\pi^+ + \pi^- + \pi^0$; $3\pi^0$

baryons

Nucleon	$\{$ p	$\bar{\text{p}}$	1/2	938.213 ± 0.01	stable	
	n	$\bar{\text{n}}$	1/2	939.507 ± 0.01	$(1.013 \pm 0.029) \times 10^3$	$\text{p} + \text{e}^- + \bar{\nu}$
Λ Hyperon	Λ	$\bar{\Lambda}$	1/2	1115.36 ± 0.14	$(2.205 \pm 0.086) \times 10^{-10}$	$\text{p} + \pi^-; \text{n} + \pi^0$
						$\text{p} + \text{e}^- + \bar{\nu}$
Σ Hyperon	$\{$ Σ^+	$\bar{\Sigma}^+$	1/2	1189.40 ± 0.20	$(0.81 \pm 0.06) \times 10^{-10}$	$\text{p} + \pi^0; \text{n} + \pi^+$
	Σ^0	$\bar{\Sigma}^0$	1/2	1191.5 ± 0.5	$< 0.1 \times 10^{-10}$	$\Lambda + \gamma$
	Σ^-	$\bar{\Sigma}^-$	1/2	1195.96 ± 0.30	$(1.61 \pm 0.10) \times 10^{-10}$	$\text{n} + \pi^-$
Ξ Hyperon	Ξ^0	$\bar{\Xi}^0$	?	1311 ± 8	1.5×10^{-10} (1 event)	$\Lambda + \pi^0$
	Ξ^-	$\bar{\Xi}^-$	?	1318.4 ± 1.2	$(1.28 \pm 0.34) \times 10^{-10}$	$\Lambda + \pi^-$

[a] Masses and mean lifetimes are taken from the Berkeley compilations.[1] Branching ratios for K-meson decay are based on the xenon bubble chamber results.[2]

quantum mechanics a particle can have no component of orbital angular momentum in the direction of its motion, it is clear that the spin of the Λ^0 can have no component in the beam direction even as neither the initial π-p state nor the final Λ^0-K state can have any component of orbital angular momentum in this direction. Since the decay products of the lambda, the nucleon, and the pion cannot carry away orbital angular momentum in the direction of its decay, and since the lambda spin must, from the preceeding argument, be perpendicular to the beam direction, there will be a deficit of lambda decays perpendicular to the beam if the lambda spin is greater than one half. Since the distribution of decays for such lambdas is known to be isotropic, it follows that the lambda spin is one half.

A more exact calculation is straightforward.[5] Taking the direction of quantization as the beam direction, and considering only those protons whose spin component in the beam direction, or z-direction, is $+1/2$, the final state wave function can be written as:

$$\sum_l \sum_m a_{lm}\, \Theta_l{}^m\, I_j{}^{1/2-m} \tag{1}$$

where the a's are complex constants, the $\Theta_l{}^m$ are the spherical harmonics representing the orbital angular momentum and the $I_j{}^n$ represent the wave function of the lambda with spin j and z-component n. The restriction to events produced in the forward and backward direction limits the sum over m solely to the terms with $m = 0$, as $\Theta_l{}^m \approx \sin^m \theta$ for small values of θ, the angle between the beam direction and the direction of production. Therefore, only the $I_j{}^{1/2}$ lambda wave function will contribute to the decays; then the wave function is:

$$
\begin{aligned}
\alpha(&\langle 1/2,\, j\, +\, 1/2,\, 1/2,\, 0 \mid 1/2,\, j\, +\, 1/2,\, j,\, 1/2\rangle Y_{j+1/2}{}^0\uparrow \\
&+\langle 1/2,\, j\, +\, 1/2,\, -1/2,\, 1 \mid 1/2,\, j\, +\, 1/2,\, j,\, 1/2\rangle Y_{j+1/2}{}^1\downarrow) \\
+\beta(&\langle 1/2,\, j\, -\, 1/2,\, 1/2,\, 0 \mid 1/2,\, j\, -\, 1/2,\, j,\, 1/2\rangle Y_{j-1/2}{}^0\uparrow \\
&+\langle 1/2,\, j\, -\, 1/2,\, -1/2,\, 1 \mid 1/2,\, j\, -\, 1/2,\, j,\, 1/2\rangle Y_{j-1/2}{}^1\downarrow)
\end{aligned}
\tag{2}
$$

where the symbols $\uparrow$ and $\downarrow$ represent the protons with spins in the plus and minus z-direction, respectively, and the normalization is such that $\alpha^2 + \beta^2 = 1$. Conservation of parity is not assumed. The two terms represent final states of different parity. From Minami's theorem,[6] the angular distributions of the decays from the two pure eigenstates of parity, with $\alpha = 0$ or $\beta = 0$, are the same. It is also true that if the initial proton is unpolarized, the interference term between the two states will vanish.

If the odd (or even) state is written as $|\psi\rangle$, the state $(\bar{\sigma}\cdot\bar{\theta})\,|\psi\rangle$ is the even (or odd) state with the same angular momentum. Here $\bar{\sigma}$ is the nucleon spin operator, and $\bar{\theta} = \bar{p}/|\bar{p}|$ where $\bar{p}$ is the nucleon momentum in the center of mass system. The operator $\bar{\sigma}\cdot\bar{\theta}$, which is then the nucleon spin operator in the nucleon production direction, changes the parity since the operator is odd under space inversion, leaves the angular momentum unchanged since the operator is invariant under rotation, and leaves the intensity distribution unchanged since the operator is unitary. Then $I = [\alpha + \beta(\bar{\sigma}\cdot\bar{\theta})]|\psi\rangle$, and the angular distribution will be: $dN/d\Omega = \langle\psi|\psi\rangle + 2\,\mathrm{Re}\,\alpha\,\beta\cos\theta\cdot F_j$, here F_j is an even function of $\cos\theta$ and θ is the angle between the decay direction and the direction of quantization. For an average of initial states with proton spin component of $+1/2$ and $-1/2$, equivalent to opposite directions of quantization, the term in $\cos\theta$ drops out and $dN/d\Omega = \langle\psi|\psi\rangle$, which is just the distribution for parity conserving decay. For different values of the spin j, the angular distributions are:

$$j = 1/2,\ dN/d\Omega = (4\pi)^{-1};\qquad j = 3/2,\ dN/d\Omega = (4\pi)^{-1}$$

$$(1/2 + 3/2\cos^2\chi);\qquad j \to \infty,\ dN/d\Omega = (4\pi)^{-1}\,(\pi\cdot\sin\chi)^{-1};$$

where χ is the angle between the decay proton in the Λ^0 center of mass and the beam direction. Of course, no events are produced at angle such that $\theta = 0$ or $\theta = 2\pi$ exactly, but from the uncertainty principle, we can consider events such that $\theta \leqslant 1/l_{\max}$ where $l_{\max}$ is the largest angular momentum we expect to be important in the production process. A reasonable estimate of

$l_{\max}$ is $p/m_{\pi}c$, where p is the final state center of mass momentum and m_{π} is the mass of the pion; $l_{\max}$ is then the largest angular momentum allowed classically to be emitted with momentum p from a region of radius of $\hbar/m_{\pi}c$. Again, the observed isotropy of decays selected using this criterion indicate that the lambda spin is 1/2. Similar reasoning, and similar experimental results, show that the sigma spin is also 1/2.[7]

A variation of this method[8] considers the reactions $K^- + p \rightarrow \Lambda^0$ (or Σ) $+ \pi$ which occur when K-mesons are stopped in liquid hydrogen. If the K^- mesons are captured by the protons from the atomic S-state, the component of hyperon spin in the direction of flight of the hyperons must be the same as the spin component of the initial proton, and the angular distribution of hyperon decays will depend upon hyperon spin as in the previous discussion. It is likely that almost all K-mesons are captured from S-states (Section 3.5) and the isotropy[9] of the decays of sigma and lambda hyperons produced by the capture of K^--mesons in hydrogen then firmly establishes the spin of these particles as 1/2, if the K-meson spin is zero.

There is also evidence concerning the spin of the lambda which does not involve the spin of the K-meson: there is particularly rigorous evidence from analyses of the decay of polarized lambdas (Section 4.3). and there is information (Section 3.7) derived from consideration of the ratio of mesonic to nonmesonic decays of light hypernuclei.

Since the hyperons are fermions, they will, in general, have a definite magnetic moment and the value of the anomalous part of this moment will depend upon the details of strong interaction dynamics. Though the lifetimes of these particles are short, measurements of the magnetic moments are practical for those particles which are found to be strongly polarized by some production mechanism, and which decay preferentially with respect to their spin direction—strongly exhibiting parity nonconservation in the decays. A measurement of the change in decay direction of the hyperons resulting from precession of the spin in a strong magnetic field then serves to establish the value of the moment.[10]

Preliminary measurements of the magnetic moment of the lambda, made in this way, result in a value of -1.5 ± 0.5 nuclear magnetons.[11] So large a value indicates that the $(n\mathrm{K}\Lambda)$ and the $(\Lambda\mathrm{K}\Xi)$ couplings cannot both be weak, since the pion-baryon couplings to virtual states cannot contribute to the magnetic moment if the strong interactions are charge independent.[12] Such virtual states must involve only pions, lambdas, sigmas, and pair states with the same symmetry as a pion. All of these states are symmetric in isotopic spin space about zero charge, and the contribution to the lambda magnetic moment current from any state is cancelled by the state with opposite values of T_3, the third component of isotopic spin, for each particle. For example, any contribution from the virtual transition $\Lambda^0 \rightleftharpoons \Sigma^+ + \pi^-$, is cancelled by the contribution from the transition $\Lambda^0 \rightleftharpoons \Sigma^- + \pi^+$. Under the same conditions, the magnetic moments of the Σ^+ and Σ^- will be equal and opposite, and the Σ^0-moment will be zero. These relations will not hold if K-couplings are important since neither the K, the nucleon, or the Ξ is centered at zero charge. There is no cancellation of the contribution from the virtual transition: $\Lambda^0 \rightleftharpoons \mathrm{p} + \mathrm{K}^-$, by $\Lambda^0 \rightleftharpoons \mathrm{n} + \overline{\mathrm{K}}^0$; though under some symmetry schemes there would be a cancellation from the transition: $\Lambda^0 \rightleftharpoons \Xi^- + \mathrm{K}^+$.

Since the K_1^0-meson is known to decay about one third of the time into two neutral pions, that is, identical bosons, the K-meson spin must be even; equal to 0, 2, 4, $\cdots$. Analysis of the angular distributions of the decays of the neutral K-meson, $\mathrm{K}_1^0 \rightarrow \pi^+ + \pi^-$, produced in the reaction $\pi^- + \mathrm{p} \rightarrow \Lambda^0 + \mathrm{K}^0$ can establish the K-spin in a manner similar to that used to determine the lambda spin.[5] Consider the decay of K-mesons produced in the beam direction, in reactions selected such that the lambda decays in the beam direction, or better, if the evidence from the decay asymmetry of polarized lambdas establishing the spin as $1/2$ is used (Section 4.3), the selection can include all directions of lambda decay. There will then be no component of orbital angular momentum in the beam direction, and the component of K-meson spin in the beam direction will be just the difference in spin components of the initial proton and the proton from the lambda decay. Again selecting initial states with the component of spin of the proton in the beam direction as $+1/2$, the wave function of a K-meson of spin 2 would be:

$$\Psi = \sum_m a_m \, \mathcal{E}_m \, Y_2{}^m \, (\chi, \phi) \tag{3}$$

for $m = 1, 0$. The orthonormal vectors, $\mathcal{E}_j$, $\mathcal{E}_j \mathcal{E}_k = \delta_{jk}$, are introduced to represent the orthogonality of the spin functions of the lambda decay protons, and the $Y_2{}^m (\chi, \phi)$ are the usual spherical harmonics. It is not possible to construct an isotropic distribution by any choice of the complex coefficients a. For no choice of a will the coefficients of the $\cos^2 \chi$ and $\cos^4 \chi$ terms of the decay intensity $|\Psi|^2$ both be zero. The observation that the decays of K-mesons, selected according to these prescribed restraints, is isotropic, then establishes the K-spin as zero.[13]

If the K-meson spin were not zero, isotropic decay distributions of K-mesons produced in almost any interaction should be exceptional, anisotropic decays and polarizations would be expected. The lack of observation of such effects then constitutes evidence for a K-meson spin of zero. The character of the three pion decay of the charged K-meson (Section 4.2) also suggests that the spin is zero.

Though the spin of the Ξ can presumably be determined using methods similar to those used to determine the spins of the other hyperons, there is not yet enough evidence available to establish the value of its spin.

2.4. Parity

Early experiments established the nonconservation of parity in weak interaction decays involving neutrinos by the observation of quantities which transform as pseudoscalars. If parity were conserved, the expectation value of such quantities should be zero. Observations on the decays of lambdas produced in the reaction $\pi^- + \mathrm{p} \to \Lambda^0 + \mathrm{K}^0$ show that the protons from the lambda decay are preferentially emitted in the direction of

$(\bar{p}_\pi \times \bar{p}_\Lambda)$ where $\bar{p}_\pi$ and $\bar{p}_\Lambda$ represent the vector momentum of the incident pion and lambda, respectively. The finite expectation value of the pseudoscalar $\bar{p}_p \cdot (\bar{p}_\pi \times \bar{p}_\Lambda)$ indicates that parity is not conserved.[14]

It is convenient to discuss this result further by referring to the spin of the lambda, $\bar{\sigma}_\Lambda$, an axial or pseudovector. Three pseudoscalars can then be formed $(\bar{\sigma}_\Lambda \cdot \bar{p}_\Lambda)$, $(\bar{\sigma}_\Lambda \cdot \bar{p}_\pi)$ and $(\bar{\sigma}_\Lambda \cdot \bar{p}_p)$; the first two associated with the lambda production reaction, the last relevant to the lambda decay. Since the direction of the spin is the only reference vector in the decay, any preferred direction of emission of the proton must be parallel or anti-parallel to the spin direction and demand a finite expectation value of the pseudoscalar $(\bar{\sigma}_\Lambda \cdot \bar{p}_p)$ and nonconservation of parity in the decay. If parity is conserved in production, the expectation values of the quantities $(\bar{\sigma}_\Lambda \cdot \bar{p}_\Lambda)$ and $(\bar{\sigma}_\Lambda \cdot \bar{p}_\pi)$ and hence, $(\bar{p}_p \cdot \bar{p}_\Lambda)$ and $(\bar{p}_p \cdot \bar{p}_\pi)$ must be zero. The only preferred direction allowed to the lambda spin, and, therefore, the lambda decay proton, is perpendicular to the plane of production. Conversely, observation of this relation has established, though with no great precision, that parity is conserved in the production process.[15]

Stronger conclusions regarding conservation of parity in the strong interactions involved in the production of strange particles follow from the results of experiments on parity conservation in nuclear interactions. Since a part of the force between nucleons must result from virtual intermediate states involving strange particles, such as the exchange of two K-mesons, nonconservation of parity in strange particle interactions should result in nonconservation of parity in nuclear forces. Since parity conserving nuclear forces are at least 10^6 times as strong as parity nonconserving forces,[16] the strong interactions of strange particles must be strongly parity conserving.

By convention, the proton is assigned positive parity, though, actually, only the parity product $(n \cdot \pi^- \cdot p)$ and the π^0-meson parity are known, and these are both odd. In a similar fashion, the parity of the lambda (and sigma) is not defined relative to

the nucleon pion system as parity is not conserved in the interactions which connect these states; only parity products such as
$(n \cdot K \cdot \Lambda)$ are defined. Again it is convenient to establish a convention and assign positive parity to the lambda. The sign of the
experimentally accessible triple product is then attributed to the
K-meson, and we speak of the possible signs, plus and minus, in
terms of a scalar or pseudoscalar K-meson. Since there is no
change of strangeness involved in interactions connecting the
sigma and lambda, only their relative parity can be determined.
On the other hand, the Ξ parity is well defined relative to the
nucleon, since two K-mesons connect nucleon and Ξ states, and
the parity of two K-mesons must be even.

At the present time there is no information on the parity of
the Ξ. Analyses of lambda-nucleon forces and the capture of
K-mesons in helium (Section 3.7) strongly suggest that the
K-meson is pseudoscalar.

The sign of the lambda-sigma relative parity determines the
correlation between the direction of lambda decay and the plane
of polarization of the gamma ray in the decay of polarized Σ^0-
hyperons.[17] Consider a Σ^0 polarized in the z-direction; since the
Σ-spin is $1/2$ and the decay involves only the strong and electromagnetic forces, the decay intensity must be isotropic, and for
any direction the decay amplitude can be written as the sum of
two terms: $a \uparrow \gamma_1^{-1} + b \downarrow \gamma_1^{1}$, where the arrows represent the
direction of lambda spin with respect to the decay direction, the
γ's represent left and right circularly polarized photons, and the
values of the complex constants a and b, normalized such that
$|a|^2 + |b|^2 = 1$, are determined by the condition that the z-
component of total angular momentum is $1/2$.[17] Since waves of
opposite circular polarization contribute incoherently to the
total intensity, the polarization of the lambdas is equal to
$|a|^2 - |b|^2$ and is in the direction of the Σ^0 decay. For decays in
which the lambda is emitted in the $+z$ or $-z$ direction, conservation of angular momentum allows only the wave function
$\gamma_1^{1} \downarrow$, and the lambda polarization is -1 with respect to the z-
direction, or $-\hat{n}$ for emission at $\theta = 0$, and $+\hat{n}$ for emission

at $\theta = \pi$, where $\hat{n}$ is the unit vector in the decay direction. The angular dependence must then be an odd function of θ, considering reflection about $\theta = \pi/2$, and can only be $(\hat{n} \cdot \bar{\sigma}_\Sigma) = \cos \theta$ (note that $(\hat{n} \cdot \bar{\sigma}_\Sigma)^3 = (\hat{n} \cdot \bar{\sigma}_\Sigma)$). Therefore, the polarization is equal to $-\hat{n} \cos \theta$, the average polarization in the decay direction is $1/2$, and the average polarization in the z-direction is $-1/3$.

If $|a|^2 - |b|^2 = -\cos \theta$, then $|a| = [(1 - \cos \theta)/2]^{1/2}$ and $|b| = [(1 + \cos \theta)/2]^{1/2}$. A detector of linear polarization of the gamma ray selects radiation with a specific phase, dependent upon the direction chosen by the analyzer, between the right and left circularly polarized amplitudes. This results in a specific phase relation between the lambda spins of opposite direction. The amplitude for lambdas produced in conjunction with, or observed in coincidence with such analyzed gamma rays will be $|a| \uparrow + \exp(i\phi) |b| \downarrow$, where ϕ depends upon the phase of a and b, and hence the angle θ, and also the direction of linear polarization. Such a wave function is always equivalent to a polarization of magnitude, $2 |a| \cdot |b| = \sin \theta$, in a direction perpendicular to $\hat{n}$, determined by ϕ; there will then be a polarization-polarization correlation between lambda and photon.

Consider, for example, sigma decays in the x direction; $\cos \theta = 0$. It is convenient to represent the circularly polarized gamma rays as combinations of linearly polarized gamma rays, and the longitudinally polarized lambdas as linear combinations of lambda states in the z direction $\uparrow_z$ and $-z$ direction $\downarrow_z$. Then the decay amplitude has the form:

$$(1/2) (\uparrow_z + \downarrow_z) (\bar{y} - i\bar{z}) + (1/2)e^{i\phi}(\uparrow_z - \downarrow_z) (\bar{y} + i\bar{z})$$

where the $\bar{z}$ and $\bar{y}$ represent the directions of plane polarization of the gamma rays. Now if the z-plane of photon polarization is selected, the phase of ϕ is equal to 0 and the lambdas in association are polarized in the z-direction. If the y-plane is chosen, $\phi = \pi$, and the lambda polarization will be in the $-z$ direction. As the plane of polarization is rotated $180°$, the direction of lambda polarization is rotated $360°$.

Only the electromagnetic field configuration will depend on

the relative sigma-lambda parity. The radiation will be $E\,1$ if the relative parity is odd, or $M\,1$ if it is even, and the magnetic fields for the two radiations differ in phase by $\pi/2$ in space, and by $\pi/2$ in time. The direction of the polarization-polarization correlations will then differ by 90° for the two cases. The polarization and angular distribution of the Λ^0 decay with respect to the sigma spin is independent of their relative parity. The correlations of the lambda spin presented here will be with the electric vector if the parity is odd and with the magnetic vector if the parity is even. Note here that if the sigmas are polarized in the $-z$ direction, all lambda polarizations are reversed. Unpolarized sigmas, which can be represented as equal incoherent amplitudes of sigmas polarized in the $+z$ and $-z$ directions, result then in unpolarized lambdas and a vanishing polarization-polarization correlation.

The detailed calculation is straightforward. Consider, again, the decay of a Σ^0 polarized in a z-direction. Depending on the parity, the decay will take place through an electric or magnetic dipole transition. In either case we can represent the angular part of the final state as: $-(1/3)^{1/2}X_1{}^0 \uparrow + (2/3)^{1/2}X_1{}^1 \downarrow$, where the $X_J{}^m$ are vector spherical harmonics of multipole order J; the arrows represent the lambda spin in the z-direction, and the constants are the appropriate Clebsch-Gordan coefficients representing the resolution of a state of angular momentum $1/2$ into states of angular momentum $1/2$ and 1. The vector spherical harmonics (Section 5.3) are further resolved into states of definite photon polarization and angular dependence:

$$X_1{}^0 = \sqrt{1/2}\ Y_1{}^1 \sqrt{1/2}\ (\underline{e}_x - i\underline{e}_y) - \sqrt{1/2}\ Y_1{}^{-1} \sqrt{1/2}$$

$$(\underline{e}_x + i\underline{e}_y)$$

and   (4)

$$X_1{}^1 = \sqrt{1/2}\ Y_1{}^1\ \underline{e}_z - \sqrt{1/2}\ Y_1{}^0 \sqrt{1/2}\ (\underline{e}_x + i\underline{e}_y)$$

where $\underline{e}_x$, $\underline{e}_y$, and $\underline{e}_z$ are unit vectors. Then, $\sqrt{1/2}\ (\underline{e}_x + i\underline{e}_y)$ and $\sqrt{1/2}\ (\underline{e}_x - i\underline{e}_y)$ represent right and left circularly polarized light with respect to the z-axis, $\underline{e}_z$ is linearly polarized light in the z-direction, and the constants are now the Clebsch-Gordan coefficients representing the resolution of a state of angular momentum 1, into two states, each with angular momentum 1. These states can be considered to have a correspondence to the spin and orbital angular momentum of the photon.

Since the spherical harmonics $Y_1{}^m$ have odd parity, the final state will have odd parity for the part of the electromagnetic field which is even under space inversion, and even parity for the part which is odd. Since the magnetic field transforms as a current loop, it is even under P; the electric field, transforming as the field of a charge, is odd. Then, if the relative lambda-sigma parity is odd, the polarization vectors refer to magnetic fields, if even to electric fields. In any case, the electric and magnetic fields are perpendicular to each other and to the direction of propagation.

To facilitate discussion of the decay, we combine terms, write out the spherical harmonics specifically, and for simplicity consider decays in the xz-plane, then:

$$\psi = (4\pi)^{-1/2} \left[\sqrt{1/2} \sin \theta i \varrho_y \uparrow + (\sqrt{1/2} \sin \theta \varrho_z - \sqrt{1/2} \cos \theta \, (\varrho_x + i\varrho_y)) \downarrow \right] \tag{5}$$

Since states of different spin and polarization directions contribute incoherently to the intensity, $\langle \psi | \psi \rangle$ is found to be just $1/(4\pi)$. The intensity is isotropic, as is to be expected from the decay of a spin 1/2 particle. The lambda polarization in the z-direction, $P_z = \langle \psi | \sigma_z | \psi \rangle / \langle \psi | \psi \rangle$, is $-\cos^2\theta$. The average lambda polarization in the z-direction for all decays will be just $-1/3$, the average value of $\cos^2\theta$, since the intensity is isotropic. The polarization in the x-direction, $P_x = \langle \psi | \sigma_x | \psi \rangle / \langle \psi | \psi \rangle$ is found to be $-\sin \theta \cos \theta$, and the average of the total polarization $(P_z{}^2 + P_x{}^2)^{1/2}$ for all decays is 1/2.

Polarization of lambdas produced in the x-direction, $\cos \theta = 0$, is zero; however, there is a strong correlation between the direction of lambda polarization and the direction of photon polarization just as shown in the qualitative discussion. Since the elec-

tron positron pairs produced by polarized gamma rays are preferentially produced parallel to the plane of polarization of the
electric field, a measurement of the correlation between the
plane of production of these pairs and the direction of decay of
the lambda will establish the relative sigma-lambda parity.
Similar arguments hold for the planes defined by the internally
converted Dalitz pairs except that the plane defined by the
Dalitz pairs is perpendicular to the plane defined in these calculations, and the strength of the correlation is somewhat
reduced. Experiments designed to determine these correlations
are in progress at the time of writing.

The branching ratio $(\Sigma^0 \rightarrow \Lambda^0 + e^+ + e^-)/(\Sigma^0 \rightarrow \Lambda^0 + \gamma)$
also depends on the relative $(\Sigma \Lambda)$ parity.[18] The branching ratio
should be about $1/183$ for even parity and about $1/162$ for odd
parity. Some insight into the source of this difference can be
gained by considering the form of the interaction for the production of photons and Dalitz pairs. Two vectors are available; $\bar{E}$,
the electric field, and $\bar{k}$, the lambda recoil momentum, and one
pseudovector, the baryon spin, $\bar{\sigma}$. If the relative parity is even,
the interaction must be the scalar $\bar{\sigma} \cdot (\bar{E} \times \bar{k})$; if the parity is
odd, the interaction will be the pseudoscalar $(\bar{\sigma} \cdot \bar{E})$. For small
values of m, the invariant mass of the electron-positron pair,
where explicitly $m = [(E_+ + E_-)^2 - (\bar{p}_+ + \bar{p}_-)^2]^{1/2}$, E and $\bar{p}$
representing the total energy and momentum of the electrons,
the recoil momentum $\bar{k}$ is almost equal to $\bar{k}'$, the recoil momentum associated with the emission of a photon, the matrix elements for the emission of a photon and a Dalitz pair are the same
for either parity, and the branching ratio to this part of the
lambda recoil spectrum is independent of the relative parity.
However, when m is at its maximum value, $m = M_\Sigma - M_\Lambda$,
the lambda recoil momentum is 0. Such a decay is then forbidden
for even relative parity though allowed for odd parity. A
measurement of the branching ratios for large values of m or
small values of $\bar{k}$ can then determine the relative parities.

Also, an analysis of $K^- + p \rightarrow \Sigma + \pi$ at a resonance suggests
that the relative $\Sigma\Lambda$ parity is even (Section 3.6).

2.5. Isotopic Spin

The determination of the values of the isotopic spins of the strange particles is not really separable from the question of the validity of charge independence in the interactions of strange particles, or equally, the conservation of isotopic spin in strong interactions. Strong evidence for charge independence in strange particle interactions results from examination of the capture of K$^-$ mesons by deuterons.[19] Since the deuteron has isotopic spin 0, the isotopic spin of the initial state will be just that of the K-meson. There is a theorem, the validity of which is strongly supported by intuition, which states that the complexity in space of a final state cannot be greater than that of the initial state. In particular, no final state angular distribution can contain terms in cos θ, higher than $(\cos \theta)^{2j}$ where j is the spin of the initial state.[20] Since the transformation properties of isotopic spin are the same as for angular momentum, this theorem also holds in isotopic spin space and no final state population, described as a function of T_3, can contain terms higher than $(T_3)^{2j}$. If the K-meson has an isotopic spin of 1/2, the distribution of pions produced in the capture, independent of what baryon states are involved, can be written as $dN(T_3) = a + bT_3$, where a and b are constants. The immediate consequence is that there will be twice as many charged as neutral pions produced. The experimental ratio is 2.07$\pm$.07, in agreement with the assumption that the reaction is charge independent and that the K-meson isotopic spin is 1/2, independent of the isotopic spins of the hyperons. There is little information from reactions concerning the isotopic spins of other strange particles, though from the multiplicities of states it is reasonably clear that for the lambda, $T = 0$; sigma, $T = 1$; and Ξ, $T = 1/2$.

2.6. K^0-Mesons

Important and interesting consequences result from the conclusion that the isotopic spin of the K-meson is 1/2. Since positive, negative, and neutral K-mesons exist, there must be two doublets, related as antiparticles: K^+ and K^0, and $\overline{K}^0$ and $\overline{K}^+$ or K^-. The K^+ and K^0 have strangeness of $+1$ and third components of isotopic spin equal to $+1/2$ and $-1/2$, respectively; while the $\overline{K}^0$ and K^- have a strangeness number of -1, and third components of $+1/2$ and $-1/2$.[21]

As a consequence of the CPT theorem, the K^0 and its antiparticle, the $\overline{K}^0$, have exactly the same mass. Though these degenerate states are eigenstates of strangeness with eigenvalues or strangeness numbers of $+1$ and -1, they are not eigenfunctions of CP. Under CP, the two states transform into one another as $CP|K^0\rangle = \exp(i\alpha)|\overline{K}^0\rangle$, and $CP|\overline{K}^0\rangle = \exp(-i\alpha)|K^0\rangle$ since the charge conjugation operator changes particle to antiparticle and the unitary parity operator at most changes the phase. The linear combinations: $|K_1^0\rangle = \sqrt{1/2}\,(|K^0\rangle + \exp(i\alpha)|\overline{K}^0\rangle)$ and $|K_2^0\rangle = \sqrt{1/2}\,(|K^0\rangle - \exp(i\alpha)|\overline{K}^0\rangle)$, are eigenfunctions of CP with eigenvalues of $+1$ and -1, respectively, but not eigenfunctions of strangeness. The relative phase of the states $|\overline{K}^0\rangle$ and $|K^0\rangle$ can be chosen such that $\alpha = 0$ with no loss of generality.

When production mechanisms are concerned, initial states are usually not eigenstates of CP, but are eigenstates of strangeness, and it is useful to consider production of K^0 and $\overline{K}^0$. However, since strangeness is not conserved in the weak decay processes, and since it will be seen that the important two pion decay mode is an eigenstate of CP, it is desirable to consider the decay of the K_1^0 and K_2^0.

Since the π^0 is self-conjugate—its own antiparticle—and since states of two π^0 mesons must have even parity, it is clear that such states are even under the CP transformation. Consider neutral combinations of charged pions like π^+ and π^-. The charge conjugation operator C changes π^+ to π^-, and π^- to π^+, and the parity operator, P, changing the coordinate r to $-r$, exchanges the position of the two particles leaving the state just as it was originally. Therefore, such a state is even under CP.

If, then, the weak interactions are invariant under time reversal, from the CPT theorem, they must be invariant under CP, and only the $K_1{}^0$ can then decay via the two pion mode. The lifetime for this transition is about 10^{-10} seconds, while the transition rates for competing modes, available to the $K_2{}^0$, lead to a lifetime of about $5 \cdot 10^{-7}$ seconds. These very different lifetimes lead us to consider the $K_1{}^0$ and the $K_2{}^0$ as particles, rather than the K^0 and $\overline{K}{}^0$. It is to be emphasized that this behavior is a consequence of the doublet isotopic spin character of the K-meson which is in turn demanded by the strangeness theory. The experimental verification of the existence of the long-lived $K_2{}^0$ meson, which did not decay into two pions, was then a striking verification of the theory.[22]

A number of interesting consequences follow from the properties of the neutral K-mesons. Since strangeness is conserved in production processes, invariably either the strangeness $+1$, K^0, or strangeness -1, $\overline{K}{}^0$, is produced. Writing these as linear combinations of $K_1{}^0$ and $K_2{}^0$; e.g., $|K^0\rangle = \sqrt{1/2}\,(|K_1{}^0\rangle + |K_2{}^0\rangle)$, we have equal intensities of $K_1{}^0$ and $K_2{}^0$ mesons. These states have different lifetimes, and in general, slightly different masses. Consider the wave function, in some specific direction, at a time t after production of the strangeness plus one K^0-mesons. Writing the masses of the $K_1{}^0$ and $K_2{}^0$ as $\hbar\omega_1/c^2$ and $\hbar\,\omega_2/c^2$, and the lifetimes as $2\tau_1 = 1/\lambda_1$, and $2\tau_2 = 1/\lambda_2$, the time dependent wave function will have the form:

$$\psi = 2^{-1/2}\,[|K_1{}^0\rangle \exp\,(-i\omega_1 t - \lambda_1 t) \\ + |K_2{}^0\rangle \exp\,(-i\omega_2 t - \lambda_2 t)] \tag{6}$$

We find, for times $t \gg \tau_1$, an almost pure $K_2{}^0$ beam. Noting that $|K_1{}^0\rangle = 2^{-1/2}(|K_0\rangle + |\bar{K}_0\rangle)$, and $|K_2{}^0\rangle = 2^{-1/2}\,(|K_0\rangle - |\bar{K}{}^0\rangle)$, it is clear that half of the intensity is in the strangeness plus one K^0-state and half in the strangeness minus one $\bar{K}{}^0$-state. For times, t, of the order of τ_1 and very much smaller than τ_2, we can put $\exp\,(-\lambda_2 t) = 1$, and we have, for the intensity of the $\bar{K}{}^0$ and K^0 states as a function of time:

$$4\langle \bar{K}^0|\psi\rangle^2 = 1 + \exp (-2\lambda_1 t)$$

$$- 2 \exp (-\lambda_1 t) \cos (\omega_1 - \omega_2)t$$

and   (7)

$$4\langle K^0|\psi\rangle^2 = 1 + \exp (-2\lambda_1 t)$$

$$+ 2 \exp (-\lambda_1 t) \cos (\omega_1 - \omega_2)t.$$

The last term in these relations represent an oscillation of the intensity between the $\bar{K}^0$ and K^0 state caused by the $K_1{}^0 - K_2{}^0$ mass difference (see Fig. 4-2).

The behavior of the neutral K-meson beam is analogous to certain classical behavior of polarized light; left and right polarized light can be considered to correspond to the K^0 and $\bar{K}^0$ states, while x and y linearly polarized light corresponds to the $K_1{}^0$ and $K_2{}^0$ states. The change of the K^0 state with time or distance is then similar to the change in left-circular polarized light (K^0) produced by passing through a medium which is both dichroic, like polaroid, preferentially absorbing the x-component ($K_1{}^0$ decay), and double refractive, like calcite, with a different index of refraction for the x and y polarized light (corresponding to the effect of the different masses of the $K_1{}^0$ and $K_2{}^0$). In passing through the medium, the proportion of left and right polarized light will oscillate as the relative phase of the x and y polarized components changes, until all of the x-polarized light is absorbed and only the y-polarized light ($K_2{}^0$) is left. This remainder can be considered, of course, a linear combination of equal parts of left and right polarized light, (K^0 and $\bar{K}^0$).

Since the K^0 and $\bar{K}^0$ part of a pure $K_2{}^0$ beam have different strangeness numbers, they will be affected differently in strong interactions. After the scattering of a $K_2{}^0$ meson the K-meson wave function, in some specific direction, can be written: $\sqrt{1/2} \ (S|K^0\rangle - \bar{S}|\bar{K}^0\rangle)$, where the quantities S are complex numbers of modulus less than or equal to one, representing the effects of absorption and phase change. Rewriting this in terms of $K_2{}^0$ and $K_1{}^0$ states, we have for the intensity of $K_1{}^0$: 1/4

$|S - \bar{S}|^2$, and for $K_2{}^0$: $1/4|S + \bar{S}|^2$. The $K_1{}^0$ mesons are recreated if there is a difference in the interaction of states of different strangeness.[23]

An interesting related phenomena involves the coherent forward scattering of $K_2{}^0$-mesons from the nucleons in bulk matter.[24] This interaction is treated very much as an interaction with an optical medium with a real and complex index of refraction— an index of refraction related to the forward scattering amplitude from the interaction centers, as is the case with electromagnetic phenomena. It is convenient to describe the interaction as the result of an "optical" potential with a depth, described in wave numbers, as $k_0 + i\kappa_0$. The intensity of a plane wave will be reduced to e^{-1} of its original value in a distance $(2\kappa_0)^{-1}$ but this mean free path must also equal $(n\sigma)^{-1}$, where n is the number of nuclei per unit volume and σ is the total cross section. From the optical theorem, $\sigma = 4\pi \, k^{-1} \, \mathrm{Im}A$, where A is the forward scattering amplitude and k the wave number of the particle or wave. Then, $\kappa = 2\pi \mathrm{Im}A \cdot nk^{-1}$, and by analytic continuation: $k = 2\pi \mathrm{Re}A \cdot nk^{-1}$.

The wave function for a $K_2{}^0$ with momentum $p = \hbar \cdot k$ can be expressed as: $\psi = 2^{-1/2} \, (|K^0\rangle \, e^{ikz} - |\bar{K}^0\rangle \, e^{ikz})$. Upon entering matter, these wave numbers will be modified by the optical potential. Since the interaction of states $|K^0\rangle$ and $|\bar{K}^0\rangle$ of different strangeness must be quite different, the effective potentials acting on these states will be different. Writing the new wave numbers as $\bar{\eta} + i\bar{\kappa}$ and $\eta + i\kappa$ for $\bar{K}^0$ and K^0, we can consider the amplitude after passing through a thickness of material z, where for simplicity, we assume that z is small compared to the mean decay length of the $K_1{}^0$. Now the intensities of $K_1{}^0$ can be found by expanding the K^0 and $\bar{K}^0$ states as before, to be: $1/4 \, (e^{-2\kappa z} + e^{-2\bar{\kappa}z} - 2\cos(\eta - \bar{\eta}) \, e^{-\kappa z}e^{-\bar{\kappa}z})$. That is, $K_1{}^0$ particles will be produced in the beam direction with the same momentum as the original $K_2{}^0$ beam. Since this is a result of coherent additions to the $K_1{}^0$ amplitude from scattering centers distributed over a macroscopic distance, this effect will not occur if the $K_1{}^0$ amplitude does not stay sensibly in phase with the $K_2{}^0$ beam.

If the $K_2{}^0 - K_1{}^0$ mass difference is large, the waves will not be in phase, and no significant intensity of $K_1{}^0$ mesons will be produced. The establishment of the effect by the observation of $K_1{}^0$ decays induced by an iron plate in a beam of $K_2{}^0$-mesons was an important proof that the $K_1{}^0 - K_2{}^0$ mass difference is not large.[25]

REFERENCES

1. W. H. Barkas and A. H. Rosenfeld, *Proceedings of the 1960 Annual International Conference on High Energy Physics at Rochester*, Interscience, New York, 1960. See also, G. A. Snow and M. M. Shapiro, *Rev. Mod. Phys.*, 33, 231 (1961).

2. B. P. Roe, D. Sinclair, G. L. Brown, D. A. Glaser, J. A. Kadyk, and G. H. Trilling, *Phys. Rev. Letters*, 7, 346 (1961).

3. M. Gell-Mann, *Phys Rev.*, 92, 833 (1953); T. Nakano and K. Nishijima, *Progr. Theoret. Phys. (Kyoto)*, 10, 581 (1953).

4. B. d'Espagnat and J. Prentki, *Nucl. Phys.*, 1, 33 (1956); J. Schwinger, *Phys. Rev.*, 104, 1164 (1956).

5. R. K. Adair, *Phys. Rev.*, 100, 1540 (1955); M. I. Shirokov, *J. Exptl. Theoret. Phys. USSR*, 31, 734 (1956).

6. S. Hayakawa, M. Kawaguchi, and S. Minami, *Progr. Theoret. Phys. (Kyoto)*, 11, 332 (1954). We use the Dyson-Nambu treatment as presented by H. A. Bethe and F. de Hoffmann, *Mesons and Fields*, Vol. II, Row, Peterson and Co., Evanston, 1955.

7. F. Eisler, R. Plano, A. Prodell, N. Samios, M. Schwartz, J. Steinberger, P. Bassi, V. Borelli, G. Puppi, H. Tanaka, P. Waloschek, V. Zoboli, M. Conversi, P. Franzini, I. Mannelli, R. Santangelo, V. Silvestrini, G. L. Brown, D. A. Glaser, and C. Graves, *Nuovo Cimento*, 7, 222 (1958).

8. S. B. Treiman, *Phys. Rev.*, 101, 1216 (1956).

9. J. Leitner, P. Nordin, Jr., A. Rosenfeld, F. Solmitz, and R. Tripp, *Phys. Rev. Letters*, 3, 238 (1959).

10. T. D. Lee and C. N. Yang, *Phys. Rev.*, 108, 1645 (1957); M. Goldhaber, *Phys. Rev.*, 101, 1828 (1956).

11. R. L. Cool, E. W. Jenkins, T. F. Kycia, D. A. Hill, L. Marshall, and R. A. Schluter, unpublished Brookhaven National Laboratory Preprint No. 6121, May, 1962. See *Phys. Rev.*, 127, 2223 (1962).

12. H. Katsumori, *Progr. Theoret. Phys. (Kyoto)*, 18, 375 (1957); R. Marshak, S. Okubo, and E. Sudarshan, *Phys. Rev.*, 106, 599 (1957); R. H. Capps, *Phys. Rev.*, 114, 920 (1959).

13. F. Crawford, Jr., M. Cresti, M. Good, M. Stevenson, and H. Ticho, *Phys. Rev. Letters*, 2, 114 (1959).

14. F. S. Crawford, Jr., M. Cresti, M. Good, K. Gottstein, E. Lyman, F. Solmitz, M. Stevenson, and H. Ticho, *Phys. Rev.*, 108, 1102 (1957); F. Eisler, R. Plano, A. Prodell, N. Samios, M. Schwartz, J. Steinberger, P. Bassi, V. Borelli, G. Puppi, G. Tanaka, P. Waloschek, V. Zoboli, M. Conversi, P. Franzini, I. Mannelli, R. Santangelo, V. Silverstrini, D. Glaser, C. Graves, and M. Perl, *Phys. Rev.*, 108, 1353 (1957); also for the decays $\Sigma^+ \to p + \pi^0$, B. Cork, L. Kerth, W. Wenzel, J. Cronin, and R. Cool, *Phys. Rev.*, 120, 1000 (1960).

15. F. Crawford, M. Cresti, M. Good, F. Solmitz, and M. Stevenson, *Phys. Rev. Letters*, 1, 418 (1958); also R. Lander, W. Powell, and H. White *Phys. Rev. Letters*, 3, 236 (1959); and J. Leitner, P. Nordin, Jr., A. Rosenfeld, F. Solmitz, and R. Tripp, *Phys. Rev. Letters*, 3, 238 (1959).

16. R. Haas, L. Leipuner, and R. Adair, *Phys. Rev.*, 116, 1221 (1959), show that the strength of *NPC* forces is proportional to $N^{1/2}F$ where N is the level spacing in a nucleus and F is the relative magnitude of the pseudoscalar part of a transition from a state of the nucleus. A reevaluation of the numerical conclusion of their experiment (that *NPC* forces have a strength $< 10^{-8}$ of parity conserving forces) in the light of work by R. J. Blin-Stoyle, *Phys. Rev.*, 118, 1605 (1960), and *Phys. Rev.*, 120, 181 (1960) suggests a weaker limit of 10^{-6}. Other work is reviewed by D. Wilkinson, *Phys. Rev.*, 109, 610 (1957).

17. R. Gatto, *Phys. Rev.*, 109, 610 (1957); G. Feldman and T. Fulton, *Nucl. Phys.*, 8, 106 (1958); N. Byers and H. Burkhardt, *Phys. Rev.*, 121, 281 (1961); G. Snow and J. Sucher, *Nuovo Cimento*, 18, 195 (1960); B. Valvev and B. Geshkenbein, *J. Exptl. Theoret. Phys. USSR*, 12, 728 (1961); L. Michel and H. Rouhaninejad, *Phys. Rev.*, 122, 242 (1961).

18. G. Feinberg, *Phys. Rev.*, 109, 1019 (1958); G. Feldman and T. Fulton, *Nucl. Phys.*, 8, 106 (1958).

19. D. Miller, J. Murray, N. Horowitz, O. Dahl, M. Schwartz, and H. Taft, as reported by L. Alvarez, *Proceedings of Ninth Annual International Conference on High Energy Physics*, Academy of Sciences, U.S.S.R., 1960.

20. E. Eisner and R. G. Sachs, *Phys. Rev.*, 72, 680 (1947).

21. M. Gell-Mann and A. Pais, *Phys. Rev.*, 97, 1387 (1955); T. D. Lee, R. Oehme, and C. N. Yang, *Phys. Rev.*, 106, 340 (1957).

22. K. Lande, E. Booth, J. Impeduglia, L. Lederman, and W. Chinowski, *Phys. Rev.*, 103, 1901 (1956); M. Bardon, K. Lande, L. Lederman, and W. Chinowski, *Annals of Physics (New York)*, 5, 156 (1958).

23. A. Pais and O. Piccioni, *Phys. Rev.*, 100, 1487 (1955).

24. M. L. Good, *Phys. Rev.*, 110, 550 (1958).

25. R. Good, R. Matsen, F. Muller, O. Piccioni, W. Powell, H. White, W. Fowler, and R. W. Birge, *Phys. Rev.*, 124, 1223 (1961).

CHAPTER 3

Strong Interactions

Two particular complementary aims dominate studies of the strong interaction, including the strong interactions of strange particles. One of these aims concerns the search for higher symmetries, symmetries other than those derived from charge independence, in the strong interactions. The other concerns what is essentially an endeavor to establish a basis for the understanding, at least in principle, of all dynamics of elementary particles in terms of a few constants, the masses, spins, isotopic spins, etc., of the particles, together with a set of coupling constants relevant to the fundamental interactions. Among the bases of the main theoretical work concerned with the latter problems is the principle of microscopic causality (no matter how short the distance, signals never travel faster than the velocity of light) from which dispersion relations are derived and conjectured— dispersion relations which are similar in some respects to those derived by Kramers and Kronig for light.[1] This extensive body of theory, usually given the name dispersion theory, tends then to supplement and complement the use of perturbation calculations of field theory in relating scattering and production amplitudes to coupling constants and to the parities of strange particles.

3.1. Symmetries

Any general faith in the existence of an underlying simplicity in the universe suggests that some more nearly unified view of mesons and baryons and their interactions must exist rather than that implied by considering all particles separately as

38

fundamental. Though a number of possible symmetries have been discussed,[2] the validity of none of these has been established.

Some aspects of general problems concerning symmetries are conveniently illustrated by discussing a particular important conjecture called global symmetry, which postulates the equivalence of all pion-baryon couplings. In the absence of symmetry-breaking K-couplings and the electromagnetic forces, the eight quasistable baryon states, the nucleon, the lambda, the sigma, and the Ξ, would have the same self energy and the same mass. Being different states of the same particle, they would also have the same spin and, inasmuch as it is operationally defined, the same parity. Furthermore, certain relations between production amplitudes should obtain, most notably, the reaction $\pi^+ + p \rightarrow \Sigma^+ + K^+$, which is observed, should be forbidden; and systems with strangeness -1 or -2 should show analogues in their excited states of spin $3/2$ corresponding to the nucleon ($T = 3/2$, $J = 3/2$) isobar. The existence and character of underlying symmetries may not be easily deduced, however, particularly if symmetry-breaking interactions are strong. Indeed, if the whole interaction is divisible into two or more interactions of similar strength, perhaps, for example, pion-baryon and K-baryon interactions, each of which involves different symmetries, the analysis may prove to be difficult.

Figure 3-1 illustrates well-established baryon and meson states as states of an energy level diagram. States stable with respect to strong interactions are presented as heavy solid lines; states which are unstable as dashed lines. Certain thresholds are indicated by dotted lines. It is immediately evident that the number of states is large (though many states are certainly not yet experimentally established) and that any symmetry stronger than charge independence is not clearly evident. More precisely, if any high symmetry, such as global symmetry, exists, the symmetry breaking forces result in splittings of otherwise degenerate states which are of the magnitude of the pion mass and comparable to the average level spacing.

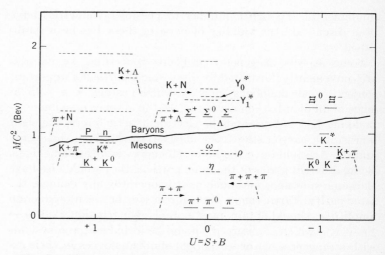

Fig. 3-1. Mass spectra for meson and baryon states versus hypercharge U, where hypercharge equals strangeness plus baryon number. Solid lines represent states stable with respect to strong interactions, dotted lines represent unstable states. The dotted arrows show important thresholds.

When the splittings are quite small, as is the case for the electromagnetic splittings, there is little difficulty in identifying either the relationships between bound states, such as the Σ^+, Σ^0, Σ^-, or excited states such as the Y^* plus, neutral, and minus, or the dynamic predictions derived from charge independence. If electromagnetic forces were stronger, if α were equal to 1/10 instead of 1/137, these indications of charge independence would be much less clear. Even as large splittings obscure the identification of corresponding states, they must seriously affect dynamic predictions. If the mass of the baryons is derivable entirely from self energies resulting from couplings to the various fields, the parameter (Δ/M_N), where Δ is the splitting and M_N is the baryon mass, would appear to be a reasonable measure of the importance of the symmetry-breaking interaction in the interpretation of dynamic results. While the smallness of this parameter suggests that the symmetry-breaking forces might be regarded as a perturbation and that dynamic predictions derived from the assumed symmetry might not be greatly distorted,[3] our limited understanding of the dynamics of elementary particles precludes any complete faith in such interpretations of measurements.

3.2. Dispersion Relations

The immediate importance of dispersion theory to studies of strange particles lies in attempts to make use of the theory to obtain information concerning coupling constants and particle parities. One aspect of this body of theory, closely related to the Kramers-Kronig relation, relates the real and imaginary parts of forward scattering amplitudes. Though the detailed form of these zero momentum transfer relations can be quite different for different processes and different uses, the interesting characteristics of the problem can be discussed in terms of the properties of a schematic basic relation:[4]

$$\text{Re } A(\omega) = 1/\pi \ P \int_{-\infty}^{+\infty} \frac{Im A(\omega')}{\omega' - \omega} \, d\omega' \tag{1}$$

where $A(\omega)$ represents the forward scattering amplitude at a total energy ω of the beam particle, and the principal part of the intergral is used. The imaginary part of the forward scattering amplitude can be related to the experimentally measured total cross section for systems of total spin equal to $1/2$, which is the case for such processes as K-nucleon scattering, by the optical theorem, $ImA = k\sigma_t/4\pi$, where k is the wave number. The integrand over the interval $m \leqslant \omega \leqslant \infty$, where m is the mass of the scattered particle, can be determined from examination of the total cross section measurements, while the integral over the region $-m \geqslant \omega \geqslant -\infty$ is determined similarly from the total cross sections of the antiparticle. From the unphysical region, $-m \leqslant \omega \leqslant m$, there will be contributions from energy-conserving processes, particularly those associated with bound states. For example, in K^- proton scattering the reaction

$K^- + p \rightarrow \Lambda^0$ will contribute. In the center of mass system, $\omega_K + (p^2 + M_p^2)^{1/2} = M_\Lambda$, where p is the momentum in the center of mass system. The total energy of the K-meson then is equal to $(M_\Lambda^2 - M_p^2 + M_K^2)/2M_\Lambda$, or 0.29 Gev. The contribution to the integral from this pole is proportional to the (p,K,Λ) coupling constant; indeed this can serve as a definition of the coupling constant, and the sign is determined by the $(pK\Lambda)$ parity. Now if the real part of the forward scattering amplitude is known with sufficient accuracy at a sufficient number of energies, these relations can be used to determine the sign and magnitude of contributions from the unphysical region, determining in this way coupling constants and parities. Using the optical theorem (Section 5.4), $d\sigma/d\Omega\ (0) = (k\sigma_t/4\pi)^2 \times (\mathrm{Re}\ A(0))^2$, measurements of the differential cross section in the forward direction, together with total cross section measurements, largely provide the necessary information. It is desirable to emphasize again the schematic nature of this discussion; considerations of symmetry and convergence result in more complex relations than those discussed here, though they are similar in principle and application.

A conjecture of Mandelstam[5] concerning the extension of collision amplitudes into the complex plane as functions of energy and momentum transfer has introduced a greatly extended use of dispersion relations and in particular has emphasized the importance and practicality of the analysis of peripheral collisions in terms of the coupling constants and parity of an intermediate particle.

Consider, for example, a reaction $A + B \rightarrow C + D$, ignoring, for simplicity, internal degrees of freedom due to spin and charge multiplicities. The scattering amplitude can then be defined in terms of three invariants:

$$s_1 = (p_A + p_B)^2 = (p_C + p_D)^2$$
$$s_2 = (p_A + p_C)^2 = (p_D + p_B)^2$$

and   (2)

$$s_3 = (p_A + p_D)^2 = (p_B + p_C)^2$$

where the p's are the four momenta of the particles in the center of mass system. Only two of these quantities are independent since

$$\sum_{j=1}^{3} s_j = \sum_{i}^{4} m_i^2$$

where m_i represents the mass of particle i. The quantity, s_j, where j represents the incoming or outgoing pair, is just equal to the square of the center of mass energy, while the other s_i represent the squares of four-momentum transfers. Typically, s, as a four-momentum transfer is equal to $p^2 + p'^2 + 2pp' \cos \theta + (E - E')^2$, where the primed and unprimed quantities represent values in the incoming and outgoing channels and θ is the center of mass production angle. A basic postulate is that a single analytic function of two variables, $A(s_a, s_b)$, describes the scattering amplitude, not only for the channel A + B $\rightarrow$ C + D, but also for the channels A + $\overline{\text{C}}$ $\rightarrow$ $\overline{\text{B}}$ + D, and A + $\overline{\text{D}}$ $\rightarrow$ $\overline{\text{B}}$ + C. The choice of channel is determined only by the values of the quantities s_i. Since these physical values of s for different reactions do not overlap, the statement that a single scattering amplitude $A(s_a, s_b)$ exists is meaningful only if A is analytic and continuable into the region of unphysical values of s.

Much of the utility of the dispersion relations is derived from the existence of singularities which dominate the behavior of the scattering amplitude in their neighborhood, singularities with positions determined simply by the masses and quantum numbers of stable particles, and with strengths simply related to fundamental coupling constants and scattering cross sections. The most important of the singularities are poles and branch cuts whose effect on the scattering amplitude can be compared to the effects of point and line charges on an electrostatic field. Aside from rigorous derivations, the positions and strengths of poles can be determined from specific rules or recipes (a) if the two ingoing and two outgoing particles in any reaction channel can be linked by a stable particle of mass m and internal quantum

numbers consistent with the incoming and outgoing particle
pairs, there will be a pole in A where the s variable corresponding
to the square of the center of mass energy is equal to m^2, and
(b) the residue, which is real, and in general, the product of two
coupling constants, is just that calculated from second order perturbation theory and is the residue of the pole resulting from the
propagator in the corresponding Feynman diagram. Figures 3-2a
and 3-2b illustrate the relationship between the situations where
the pole is in the energy variable and in the momentum transfer
variable, respectively. Since the intermediate particle E is
stable, and cannot then decay into the states which it couples,
the pole is not in a physical region of total energy, nor, less
obviously, in a physical region of four-momentum transfer.

In the immediate vicinity of a pole, the scattering amplitude
is completely determined by the residue of the pole and hence
by the coupling constants. Since the pole lies outside the physical
region, the utility of this relation must depend upon extrapolation of the measured amplitudes from the physical region. If the
total energy is held constant, the remaining independent variable
is a function only of $\cos \theta$ with poles on the real $\cos \theta$ axis outside

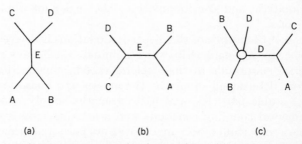

(a)   (b)   (c)

Fig. 3-2. Diagrams representing interactions: (a) represents a reaction
which has a pole in the scattering amplitude at a value of the total energy
variable of $M_E c^2$; (b) represents an interaction with a pole in the scattering
amplitude at a momentum value of the transfer variable of $M_E c^2$; (c)
represents an inelastic scattering interaction with a pole in the amplitude
for production of the particles B and D with a definite total energy, ω, at a
value of the momentum transfer variable equal to $M_D c^2$.

the interval $-1 \leqslant x \leqslant 1$, where $x = \cos \theta$. The scattering amplitude expressed as a function of x, can then be represented near a pole at $x = x_0$, by the relation $A(x) = C + R/(x - x_0)$, where R is the residue and C is a complex quantity sensibly independent of x. In the absence of other nearby singularities, an adequate procedure for extrapolation to a near pole is realized by constructing the function:

$$G^2\,(x)\, =\, (x\, -\, x_0)^2\, d\sigma/d\Omega\,(x)\, \equiv\, (x\, -\, x_0)^2\,(\mathrm{Re}\,A(x))^2 \\ +\,(x\, -\, x_0)^2\,(Im\,A(x))^2 \tag{3}$$

which is asymptotically equal to $(x - x_0)^2\,(\mathrm{Re}\,A(x))^2$ as $x \to x_0$.

Since the pole is in the real part of A, $G^2(x_0)$ is then equal to the square of the residue of the pole.

In some cases, the sign of $G^2\,(x_0)$ depends upon the parities of the particles. Consider, for example, the interaction represented by the diagram shown in Figure 3-2b. Assume that the particles A, B, C, and D are spin 1/2 baryons and that the intermediate particle E has spin 0. If the parity (A, E, C) or (B, E, D) is odd, the particle E must be absorbed or emitted at that vertex in a P-state, and the absorption or emission will be forbidden by the centrifugal barrier for four-momentum transfer equal to zero. If this nonphysical point lies between the physical region and the pole, the part of $G^2\,(x)$ resulting from the pole will change from positive to negative at this point and be negative at $x = x_0$. If the parities were both even, the absorption and emission could proceed by S-wave, the zero would not be required, and the residue would be positive.

In order that these procedures result in meaningful conclusions, it is necessary to insure that the extrapolation be reliable, a condition which is likely to occur only if the pole is sufficiently near the physical region and far from other singularities to dominate the nearby physical region.

If the pole is very near the physical region, $(|x_0| - 1)$ will be small and the contribution of the pole term to the differential cross section will depend strongly on $x = \cos \theta$. This pole contribution will then tend to dominate the high powers of cos θ in an expansion of the differential cross section and hence the interaction corresponding to high values of angular momentum or the interactions at large distances. Such interactions are dominated by the longest range force, the force involving the exchange of the lightest virtual particle or particles, which is just that described by the Feynman diagram corresponding to the singularity nearest the physical region in the dispersion theory representation. Poles and branch cuts far from the physical region, corresponding to the exchange of more massive particles, result in much less singular contributions to the physical region. The pole term then contributes lower powers of cos θ in the expansion of the differential cross sections and then to the low angular momentum, central collisions dominated by short-range forces.

A related procedure,[6] also concerned with peripheral collisions, may be useful in determining the scattering cross section for unstable particles. Consider the reaction A + B → C + D + B where the longest range interaction will be represented by the diagram of Figure 3-2c. It seems likely that the cross section for the scattering of B from D, at a total energy ω in their center of mass system, may be determined by extrapolation of the function $d^2\sigma/d(\omega^2)$ ds, where s is the square of the four momentum transfer $(p_A - p_C)^2$ from target to spectator particle, to a pole in a nonphysical region of momentum transfer where $s = m_D^2$. As in the previous discussion, this is equivalent to an extrapolation in cos θ, where cos θ is the angle of production of the pseudoparticle or complex B-D. In this case, the residue is proportional not to the square of coupling constants, but to the product of the square of the coupling constant relevant to the vertex ADC, and the cross section σ_{BD} (ω).

3.3. Production by Pions and Nucleons

Much of our knowledge of the characteristics of strange particles has been obtained from the exposure of hydrogen bubble chambers to pion beams at energies near 1 Gev. Cross sections for the production of strange particles by the interactions, pion plus nucleon yields hyperon plus K-meson, largely determined in this way, are shown together with typical angular distributions in Figure 3-3. The hyperon production cross sections are roughly equal to a millibarn and are of the order of five percent of the total pion-nucleon production cross section.[7]

In general, we have available, or can obtain, values of differential cross sections and of baryon polarizations as a function of angle and of bombarding energy. A complete description of

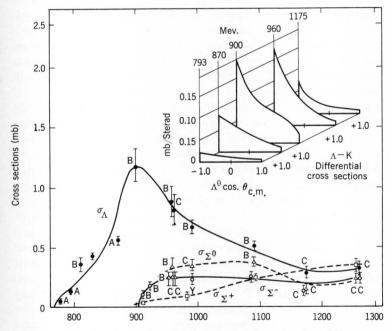

Fig. 3-3. Total cross sections for the associated production of hyperons and K-mesons in pion collisions with protons.[7] Inset shows how the differential cross section for Λ^0 production by π^- changes with energy. The points are labeled as follows: A, Brookhaven National Laboratory; B, Lawrence Radiation Laboratory; C, Columbia University; and Y, Yale University.

two-particle reaction products can be made in these terms, and, indeed, any complete theory must, in principle, be able to predict these results. No such theory exists, but techniques do exist for making a more economical and meaningful summary of the data by a representation which recognizes symmetries. For example, assuming that charge independence and hence isotopic spin conservation holds, the two independent final states given by $I = 1/2$, and $I = 3/2$ characterize strange particle production in both pion-nucleon and photo-nucleon interactions. Second, since angular momentum and parity are conserved in these reactions, kinematically independent partial waves of definite angular momentum and parity can be constructed. Since the interactions are short range, there may exist an angular momentum $l' = ka$ where k is the wave number and a an interaction radius, such that for all $l > l'$, the production amplitudes $A_l << A_{l'}$. For each $l > 0$, there are two states of total angular momentum $j = l \pm 1/2$, so there will be $(2l + 1)$ complex amplitudes. Since the over-all phase is irrelevant, the production amplitude can be described by $(4l + 1)$ constants. Angular distributions will have the form $\Sigma_i A_i \cos^i \theta$, where $i = 0, 1, \cdots 2l$, and polarizations will be proportional to $\sin \theta \Sigma_j B_j \cos^j \theta$ where $j = 0, 1, \cdots (2l - 1)$. There are then $4l + 1$ experimentally available constants which then define, at worst, discrete sets of production amplitudes at any energy.

In practice, a complete analysis of the production amplitudes in terms of partial amplitudes of definite l and j is at best difficult; and it may be impossible, as a sufficiently sharp cut off in angular momentum may not exist. However, the application of theorems concerning the behavior of partial amplitudes near threshold (Section 5.5) or at resonances (Section 3.6) may further define the amplitudes. This is the case for the particular problems of pion-nuclear prodution of lambda and sigma hyperons for pion laboratory energies below 1 Gev.

At threshold, the production amplitudes A_l vary as $Mk^{(2l+1)/2}$ $\exp (i\delta)$, where $\delta = ak^{(2l + 1)} + \phi$, k is the hyperon K wave number, and $a, \phi,$ and M are real. This relation is not likely to be nearly exact over an energy range much larger than 10 or 20 Mev, though it may serve as a useful guide extending to much higher energies. Since several reaction channels are open, δ is not simply related to the final state scattering phase shifts (Section 5.7). Very near threshold, S-wave production must dominate; the cross section must rise steeply from threshold—as k is equal to the square root of the energy above threshold, $(E - E_t)^{1/2}$; and the angular distribution must be isotropic. This behavior is exhibited by the sigma production cross sections up to pion energies approaching 950 Mev so that it seems very likely that S-wave production is dominant.

Lambda production appears to be very different from sigma production and much more complex. The variation of the cross section with energy very near threshold suggests that the part proportional to $(E - E_t)^{1/2}$, which would be associated with the S-wave, is small; and that the production, even at energies near 800 Mev, is dominated by states of higher angular momentum. However, the angular distributions up to 870 Mev are not very different from isotropic; in particular, they show no strong $\cos^2 \theta$ dependence. Only S and $P^{1/2}$ states can be isotropic; consequently, the angular distributions are consistent with the assumption that the intensity is primarily the result of production in the S-state with some P-wave impurity providing the fore-aft asymmetry, or primarily in the $P^{1/2}$ state with some S-wave. If the S and $P^{1/2}$ wave are the only important ones, the angular distributions will have the form $d\sigma/d\Omega = k_p^{-2} (|A_s|^2 + |A_p|^2 + 2 \operatorname{Re} A_s A_p \cos \theta)$, while the lambda polarization will be $2 \operatorname{Im} A_s A_p \sin \theta/(d\sigma/d\Omega)$, where k_p is the wave number of the pion-nucleon system. If the $P^{1/2}$ state is dominant at some energy above threshold, there must exist some lower energy where the S and $P^{1/2}$ amplitudes are equal, as the S-wave amplitude must be dominant at threshold. However, even at threshold the relative phase need not be near zero, the phase difference may be near 90° and the asymmetry, which is proportional to $\cos \delta$, may be small. The polarization, which is proportional to $\sin \delta$, would then be large. Indeed at this energy, where the absolute values of the amplitudes are equal, either the asymmetry or the polarization would be very large. It is not clear that this is the case.

There is no generally accepted explanation of the lambda production peak at 900 Mev. This peak coincides with a peak in the pion-nucleon total cross section at 900 Mev, and it also coincides with the threshold for sigma production, and less precisely, with the threshold for the reaction $\pi + p \rightarrow p + \rho$, where ρ is a state which decays into two pions. It is known that ρ production is important near these energies. If the peak is the result of the existence of a single resonance responsible for the total cross section maximum, a lambda-K-meson amplitude corresponding to orbital angular momentum $l = 2$, or 3 must be involved, as the height of the total pion-proton cross section peak[8] requires that the spin of the resonance state be at least 5/2. While the lambda angular distribution at 900 Mev shows a clear indication of the existence of a $\cos^3 \theta$ term, the strong $\cos^4 \theta$ term, which must result from a large intensity of a spin 5/2 state, is absent. Furthermore, the phase of a resonance amplitude will generally change by 180° passing through resonance (Section 3.6), and asymmetries and polarizations should change sign. This does not occur. Early conjectures that the peak might be a cusp (Section 5.8) resulting from the effects of the sigma threshold,[9] have not been substantiated. However, the combined effects of the sigma and ρ thresholds on a predominantly S-wave production might well account for the anomalous behavior of the Λ^0 production cross section with energy.

Since isotopic spin is conserved in the strong interactions which involve strange particles, lambda-K-meson production takes place entirely through the $T = 1/2$ pion-nucleon state while both the $T = 1/2$ and $T = 3/2$ states contribute to Σ-K production. Charge independence then imposes certain relationships between the three amplitudes for the processes $\pi^+ + p \rightarrow \Sigma^+ + K^+$, $\pi^- + p \rightarrow \Sigma^- + K^+$, and $\pi^- + p \rightarrow \Sigma^0 + K^0$, which we denote as A^+, A^-, and A^0. Since the interaction is invariant under rotation in isotopic spin space, production amplitudes A_I, dependent only on the total isotopic spin I, can represent transitions from (π,p) states to (Σ,K) states. We resolve the wave function of the initial states into states of definite isotopic spin:

$$\psi(\pi^-,\text{p}) \rightarrow \sqrt{(1/3)}\psi_{3/2}{}^{-1/2} - \sqrt{(2/3)}\psi_{1/2}{}^{-1/2} \text{ and } \psi(\pi^+,\text{p}) \rightarrow \psi_{3/2}{}^{3/2}$$

where the subscript represents the total isotopic spin and the superscript is the third component. These states undergo transitions to (Σ,K) states ϕ, with transition amplitudes A which are functions only of the total isotopic spin. Then:

$$\psi(\pi^-,\text{p}) \rightarrow \sqrt{(1/3)}A_{3/2}\phi_{3/2}{}^{-1/2}$$
$$- \sqrt{(2/3)}A_{1/2}\phi_{1/2}{}^{-1/2}; \quad \psi(\pi^+,\text{p}) \rightarrow A_{3/2}\phi_{3/2}{}^{3/2}$$

Resolving the states of definite isotopic spin into definite charge states:

$$\phi_{3/2}{}^{-1/2} = \sqrt{(2/3)}\phi_0 + \sqrt{(1/3)}\phi_-,$$
$$\phi_{1/2}{}^{-1/2} = \sqrt{(1/3)}\phi_0 - \sqrt{(2/3)}\phi_-, \ \phi_{3/2}{}^{3/2} = \phi_+$$

where the 0, $-$, and $+$ subscripts represent $(\Sigma^0 K^0)$, $(\Sigma^- K^+)$, and $(\Sigma^+ K^+)$ states. The amplitudes of states of definite charge are then:

$$A^+ = A_{3/2}, \ A^0 = ((\sqrt{2})/3)\, A_{3/2} -$$
$$((\sqrt{2})/3)\, A_{1/2}, \ A^- = 1/3\, A_{3/2} + 2/3\, A_{1/2}$$

These relations are combined to show that $(\sqrt{2})\, A^0 = A^+ - A^-$.

This last equation, relating the complex amplitudes, is called the triangle relation as the amplitudes are restricted to those which can form a triangle in the complex plane. It then follows that $(\sqrt{2})(\sigma_0)^{1/2} \leqslant (\sigma_+)^{1/2} + (\sigma_-)^{1/2}$, where σ represents the differential cross section at any angle or the total cross section. A violation of this inequality would represent a violation of charge independence.[10]

Though no violation of this inequality is known, the ratios of differential cross sections for Σ production for certain pion energies near 1.1 Gev and at certain backwards angles are such that the relation becomes nearly an equality—the triangle is flat.

Where this is the case, the polarizations of the sigmas for the three reactions must be equal.[11] Consider for convenience, sigma production at an angle θ with respect to the pion beam or z-direction. The amplitude ψ for production at an azimuthal angle ϕ equal to zero, or in the xz-plane can be written as $(\sqrt{1/2})(\psi_+ + \psi_-)$ where $\psi_+ = A{\uparrow} + B{\downarrow}$ from initial proton states with $m_z = 1/2$, and $\psi_- = A{\downarrow} - B{\uparrow}$ from proton states with $m_z = -1/2$. Since the unpolarized target protons are represented as an incoherent set of states with $m_z = 1/2$ and $-1/2$, the states ψ_+ and ψ_- are incoherent. Recalling that $\sigma_y{\uparrow} = +i{\downarrow}$, and $\sigma_y{\downarrow} = -i{\uparrow}$, where σ_y is the y component of the spin operator, the polarization in the y-direction, $P = \langle\psi|\sigma_y|\psi\rangle/\langle\psi|\psi\rangle$, is equal to $2|A|\cdot|B| \sin \delta/(|A|^2 + |B|^2)$, where δ is the phase difference between A and B. Noting that the cross section $\sigma = |\psi|^2 = |A|^2 + |B|^2$, the differential cross section triangle inequality takes the form:

$$2^{1/2}(|A^0|^2 + |B^0|^2)^{1/2} \leqslant (|A^+|^2 + |B^+|^2)^{1/2} + (|A^-|^2 + |B^-|^2)^{1/2} \tag{4}$$

where the triangle relation must hold for A and B separately. It is easy to see than an equality will occur only if both the triangles representing A and B are flat and the ratios of the amplitudes A^+/A^- and B^+/B^- are equal. Since the charge amplitudes are colinear for both A and B, the phase differences δ_0, δ_+ and δ_- are the same and $P_0 = P_+ = P_-$. Experimentally, this is particularly important for finding samples of polarized Σ^0 in determining the relative Λ^0, Σ^0 parity (Section 2.2).

It is probable that the production of strange particles in nucleon-nucleon collisions is closely related to pion-nucleon production. Interactions of nucleons with nucleons at large distances are almost surely dominated by processes which can be represented as the interaction of one nucleon with a single virtual pion emitted by the second nucleon. The absorption of the virtual pion by the nucleon results in nucleon-nucleon elastic scattering; the scattering of the pion by the nucleon results in the inelastic scattering process, $N + N \rightarrow N + N + \pi$; and pion-nucleon reactions such as strange particle production, $\pi + N \rightarrow Y + K$, result in the nucleon-nucleon processes, $N + N \rightarrow N + Y + K$, where Y represents a hyperon. Elastic scattering amplitudes at small scattering angles or for large values of the nucleon-nucleon angular momentum may be calculated with adequate precision by methods involving either extrapolation to a pole[12] in the momentum variable where the square of the four-momentum transfer is equal to m_π^2, or correspondingly in $\cos\theta$ where θ is the angle of scattering, or by perturbation theory.[13] To the extent that the approximations are valid, the results depend only upon the $(N\pi N)$ coupling constant, taken once for the pion absorption and once for the pion emission. Production amplitudes for processes such as $N + N \rightarrow Y + K + N$ can be determined in states of large orbital angular momentum of the Y-K and nucleon, or for small values of θ where θ is the angle of production of the Y-K system, in very much the same manner—either by extrapolation to a pole in the four-momentum transfer from the nucleon to the Y-K system at a value for the square of the momentum transfer of m_π^2, or by perturbation theory. In either case, the information required consists of the $(N\pi N)$ coupling constant for the pion emission, and the cross section for the reactions $\pi + N \rightarrow Y + K$ taken at the energy corresponding to the interaction of the incident nucleon with a stationary pion. This is the nonphysical kinematic situation at the pole and corresponds to an extrapolation in the laboratory kinetic energy of the spectator N_s to below zero. An illustration of the situation is shown in Figure 3-4a. The circle represents the $\pi + N \rightarrow Y + K$ interaction to all orders.

The most extensive measurements concerning the production of strange particles by nucleon-nucleon collisions are those concerning proton-proton collisions at 2.85 Gev.[14] The results of a perturbation theory calculation[15] of the contributions of this one-pion process to total hyperon production cross sections at this energy, as shown in Table 3-1, are in rather good agreement with

Table 3-1

Comparison of Hyperon Production in 2.85 Gev p-p Collisions with Theoretical Predictions[15] of the Single Pion Exchange Model[a]

Final state	Experimental, mb	π-Exchange, mb
Σ^+K^+n	$0.047\pm.012$	0.069
Σ^+K^0p	$0.030\pm.010$	$0.052\pm.016$
Σ^0K^+p	$0.013\pm.007$	0.011
Λ^0K^+p	$0.051\pm.012$	$0.053\pm.012$

[a] For completeness the other identified modes are $\Sigma^-K^+p\pi^+ = 0.003$, $\Sigma^+KN\pi = 0.004$ (Λ^0 or Σ^0) $K^+p\pi^0 = 0.011$ (Λ^0 or Σ^0) $K^0p\pi^+ = 0.014$ (Λ^0 or Σ^0) $K^+n\pi^+ = 0.002$, all in mb.

the results, suggesting that the contributions of the one-pion process may dominate the total hyperon production cross section as well as the production at small angles or at high angular momentum.

It is also possible to calculate the contribution of the single K-meson exchange process, as shown in Figure 3-4b, to the reaction $N + N \rightarrow N + K + \Lambda$ in an almost completely analogous manner. Here the necessary input information is the value of the (N, K, Y) coupling constant which is not yet known, the

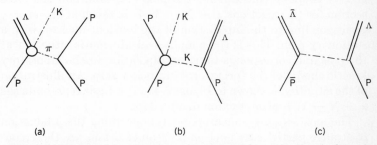

(a)   (b)   (c)

Fig. 3-4. Diagrams representing strange particle production in interactions between nucleons (a) associated production of Λ^0 and K by one pion exchange in proton-proton interaction; (b) Λ^0, K production via the exchange of a single K-meson; (c) hyperon production by the exchange of a single K-meson between proton and antiproton.

(N, K, Y) parity, and the measured K-nucleon scattering cross sections at an energy corresponding to the collision of the incident nucleon with the stationary K-meson. Here the pole exists in the four-momentum transfer of the nucleon to K-nucleon system at a value of the square of the momentum transfer of m_K^2. Even as the extrapolation in the single pion exchange case is equivalent to an extrapolation to below zero laboratory kinetic energy of the spectator nucleon, N_s, the pole in the single K-meson exchange process will correspond to the extrapolation to below zero laboratory kinetic energy of the Y-hyperon; and the contribution is, in principle, distinguishable from the single pion exchange. An examination of hyperon production in this way might then provide information on the (NKY) coupling. This has not yet been possible.

Studies, which have now commenced,[16] concerning the production of lambda-antilambda pairs by nucleon-antinucleon interactions, as shown in Figure 3-4c, may result in a measure of the K-meson coupling constant more simply. The differential cross sections at values of $\cos \theta$ near one will be strongly influenced by the nearby pole in the four-momentum transfer $(p_n - p_\Lambda)$, at $(p_n - p_\Lambda)^2 = m_K^2$. The residue of the pole will be proportional to the square of the (NKY) coupling constant and the sign will be negative if the K is pseudoscalar.

3.4. Photoproduction

Differential cross sections and excitation functions for the photoproduction of K-mesons by the reactions $\gamma + p \rightarrow K^+ + \Lambda^0$, and $\gamma + p \rightarrow K^+ + \Sigma^0$ have been measured at photon energies up to 1.2 Gev.[17] Through the final state interactions it might be expected that close relations exist between the production of strange particles by photo-nucleon and pion-nucleon interactions. To a good approximation, the center of mass energy is the same for incident photons and pions of the same total laboratory energy; therefore, photon reactions at 1000 Mev photon energy can be compared to pion reactions at a pion kinetic energy of about 860 Mev. At this energy, the total pion-nucleon cross section minus diffraction scattering is about 40 mb, of which about 1.5% represents strange particle production. The total photoproduction cross section is about 150 μb—not much different from 1/137 times the pion-nucleon cross section. The photoproduction cross section for strange particles is about 1.7 μb, or about 1.2%—a ratio which is almost the same as that for the pion-induced reactions.

Since K-mesons have zero spin and probably negative parity, the reaction $\gamma + p \rightarrow K^+ + \Lambda^0$ is in many respects analogous to the pion photoproduction reaction $\gamma + p \rightarrow \pi^+ + n$, and it is attractive to consider, for K-meson photoproduction, methods of analysis which have been informative in pion physics. In particular, it has been possible to show that in the long wave length, or zero energy limit, the Born approximation or perturbation theory calculation of pion photoproduction through the interaction of the electromagnetic field with the pion current is exact.[18] This is true in the same way, and for similar reasons, that a field theoretical perturbation calculation of Thomson scattering results, correctly, in the expected classical result. According to this calculation, the S-wave photoproduction cross section for positive pions, and hence for positive K-mesons, should be equal to $2(e^2/\hbar c)\ (g^2/\hbar c)\cdot\pi R^2\beta$, where R is the nucleon compton wave length, and β is the velocity of the pion, or K-meson, in the center of mass system. Since pions cannot be produced at zero energy, the expression is no longer exact. The most important correction for pion photoproduction is a factor approximately equal to $(1 + \mu/M)^{-2}$, where μ and M are the pion and nucleon masses. Similar, but more complicated factors obtain for K-photoproduction. With such corrections, the psuedoscalar pion-nucleon coupling constant $g^2/\hbar c$ is found to have a value of about 13. Of course, the zero energy approximation is very much worse for K-meson production, where $(M_K/M_n) \approx 1/2$, but the value of about 1 for the $(nK\Lambda)$ coupling constant derived in this way has been considered suggestive of a small K-coupling constant.

More sophisticated perturbation theory calculations[19] differ principally from the zero-energy approximation in the consideration of recoil effects which are no longer negligible; even as the mass of the K-meson is not small compared with the mass of the lambda. In particular, the interaction of the electromagnetic field with the anomalous magnetic moments of the baryons can result in large contributions to the S-wave production amplitude, obscuring the relation between the cross sections and the coupling constants. Figure 3-5 shows Feynman diagrams which are important. The circles represent the vertices where the effects of the anomalous magnetic moments are introduced as a phenomenological way of introducing important terms, which are of higher order in perturbation theory, into the calculation. The "photoelectric" transition, as shown in Figure 3-5c is independent of the magnetic moment, and in the long wavelength approximation ($M_K = 0$, $M_\Lambda = M_p$), the contribution of the anomalous magnetic moment in the "shaking off" transition of Figure 3-5a is zero, the recoil or baryon current Figure 3-5b does not contribute at all, and the results are then independent of the magnetic moments.

The amplitudes predicted by these perturbation theory calcula-

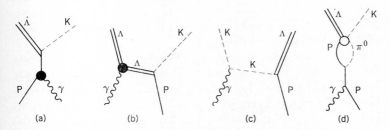

Fig. 3-5. Diagrams representing strange particle production by gamma rays incident on protons: (a) direct absorption of the gamma followed by "shaking off" of the K-meson; (b) the recoil or baryon current diagram; (c) the "photoelectric" transition; (d) production via final state interaction, $\gamma + p \rightarrow \pi^0 + p \rightarrow K^+ + \Lambda^0$. A small black circle at a vertex represents the presence of the anomalous magnetic moment of the baryon, when its effect is important.

tions for S-wave and higher angular momentum states depend strongly upon the different assumptions made concerning the (NYK) parities and the ratios of coupling constants for (NΛK) and (NΣK) interactions, and comparison of theory with experiment might resolve these questions. However, in order to be manageable, perturbation theory calculations consider only a few terms of an expansion in coupling constants, or the simplest of Feynman diagrams. Since the strong interaction coupling constants are large, perturbation theory is often inadequate. Especially, these calculations do not consider the final state interactions which include terms which can be said to represent such K-meson production mechanisms as $\gamma + \mathrm{p} \rightarrow \pi^0 + \mathrm{p} \rightarrow$ $\mathrm{K}^+ + \Lambda^0$, as in Figure 3-5d where the second process can be considered a result of a final state interaction between the pion and the nucleon. A crude estimate of this contribution, made by multiplying the known pion photoproduction cross sections of about 100μb by the probability of about 2% of a pion and nucleon interacting at this energy, at short range, to produce a K plus a lambda, suggests then a value of about 2 μb for K-meson production via the final state interaction. Since this is the same magnitude as the observed cross section, and would be coherent with the contributions from the simpler processes included in the perturbation calculations, it would seem necessary to be pessimistic concerning acceptance of even the qualitative conclusions of the perturbation calculations.

Furthermore, the absolute magnitude of S-matrix elements for the strong final state interaction indicates that they are important in determining the relative phase of the photoproduction amplitudes and very likely affect the intensity through what is essentially radiation damping. The relative phases of the various partial waves need not be zero, even at threshold. Since the total pion-nucleon cross sections at these energies are of the order of the geometric size of the nucleon, $\pi(\hbar/m_\pi c)^2$, the values of all of the S-matrix elements linking such channels as $\pi,\mathrm{p} \rightleftharpoons$ $\mathrm{n} + 2\pi$, and $\pi,\mathrm{p} \rightleftharpoons \mathrm{K},\mathrm{Y}$ are not likely to be small compared to 1, for low values of angular momentum. Because of the unitary character of the S-matrix, the cross section for the photoproduction processes will be reduced from any value calculated from a complete perturbation theory. The plausibility of this is suggested by consideration of the radiative capture of K^+-mesons by lambdas which is related to the photoproduction by detailed balance. If the cross sections for scattering of the K-mesons, and for the reactions $K^+ + \Lambda \rightarrow \pi^0 + p$ are large, these transitions will compete with the radiative capture, in perturbation theory terms, by emptying the state quickly. In detail, this competition is important if the matrix elements $|\delta_{ij} - S_{ij}|$ are not small compared to 1. A special effect of this competition will be the existence of a cusp in the Λ-K photoproduction cross section at the threshold for Σ-K photoproduction (Section 5.8). Damping effects are negligible for S-wave pion production since $|1 - S_{\pi\pi}| \equiv |1 - e^{2i\delta}| \ll 1$, where δ is the S-wave pion-nucleon scattering phase shift at low energies. No other channels are open.

Sufficiently near threshold a phenomonological description might be useful. Table 3-2 presents the momentum and angular dependence of pure low angular momentum states. In general, these are coherent and an analysis of the angular distribution is complicated. In a manner similar to the results of pion-nucleon production of strange particles, there are spin-flip amplitudes in

Table 3-2

Momentum and Angle Dependence of Pure States Produced by πp and γp Interactions Near Threshold [a]

j	l	$|A|^2_{\pi p}$	γ-Transition	$|A|^2_{\gamma p}$
1/2	0	p	$E1$	p
1/2	1	p^3	$M1$	p^3
3/2	1	$(1/2 + 3/2 \cos^2 \theta)p^3$	$M1$	$(1/2 + 3/4 \sin^2 \theta)p^3$
3/2	1	—	$E2$	$(3/4 + 3/4 \cos^2 \theta)p^3$
3/2	2	$(1/2 + 3/2 \cos^2 \theta)p^5$	$E1$	$(1/2 + 3/4 \sin^2 \theta)p^5$

[a] j represents the total angular momentum, l the orbital angular momentum, and p the center of mass momentum of the final state.

which the baryon spin direction is changed, and nonspin-flip amplitudes. For photoproduction of K-mesons, only the S-wave amplitude has no nonspin-flip term; a result obvious on inspection since the component of angular momentum along the beam of the S-wave state, $\pm 1/2$ must be made up of the difference between the nucleon component of $\pm 1/2$, and the photon component of ± 1.

The extraction of information concerning the K-meson coupling constant and the (NYK) parities by the use of perturbation theory analyses of S-and P-wave, small impact parameter, K-meson photoproduction, encounters as primary difficulties the lack of knowledge of the baryon anomalous magnetic moments, the effects of final state interactions, and the effects of radiation damping. However, these effects are not important in high angular momentum, peripheral collisions. The interaction which will dominate the K-meson photoproduction for large impact parameters is the longest range interaction. This is represented by the "photoelectric" diagram of Figure 3-5c, and is not affected by anomalous moments. At a sufficient distance, or for a sufficiently high angular momentum, all interactions are weak, all matrix elements $|\delta_{ab} - S_{ab}|$ are small, and radiation damping is not important. Perturbation theory, or what is nearly equivalent in this case, extrapolating the momentum transfer dispersion relations to a nearby pole, can then be used, in principle, to determine the (NKY) coupling constants and parities.

The one attempt to do this,[20] which is mainly expositional in nature, considers the extrapolation of data concerning the reaction $\gamma + p \rightarrow K^+ + \Lambda^0$, at 1000 Mev photon energy, to a pole at $\cos \theta = E_K/p_K c = 2.7$, where θ is the angle of production of the K-meson. Since the pole is very far from the physical region, and since the nearly isotropic production must be dominated at this low energy by S-and P-waves, the part of the differential cross section proportional to high powers in $\cos \theta$, and hence resulting from high angular momentum interactions, is masked by the experimental error. Since the contributions of these states may well be quite important at $\cos \theta = 2.7$, it is not possible to derive statistically significant information concerning the magnitude or sign of the residue at the pole, and the magnitude of the coupling constant or the sign of the (NKΛ) parity. At higher energies where the pole is nearer the physical region, an analysis of accurate data should be more reliable.

3.5. Interactions of K-Mesons with Nucleons

From the usual viewpoint of field theory, the interaction of the baryons with the meson fields may be considered as the fundamental strong interactions. All static, as well as dynamic, properties of the elementary particles are described in terms of more or less complicated transitions involving the emission and absorption of mesons by baryons. The basic form of the nucleon-pion interaction is known and the pion-nucleon pseudoscaler coupling constant $G^2/\hbar c = 13 \pm 1.5$, is established as a constant of nature. Since pions and the strange baryons are unstable, reliable information concerning pion-hyperon couplings such as that derived concerning pion-nucleon couplings from pion-nucleon scattering, etc., is not available and the information from pion-hyperon final state interactions, hyperon-nucleon scatterings, and lambda-nucleus bindings is not sufficient to establish the strength of the $(\Sigma\pi\Sigma)$ interaction or the strength or form of the $(\Lambda\pi\Sigma)$ interaction.

Nucleon–K-meson interactions can be studied directly, however. Since K-meson lifetimes are comparable to pion lifetimes, scattering experiments have been conducted using similar techniques and with accuracies comparable to those in pion experiments. Total K-nucleon cross sections[21] are shown in Figure 3-6.

Since both $S = 1$ and $S = -1$ states are involved, the K-nucleus interactions, unlike the pion-nucleon interactions, must be described in terms of scattering amplitudes of definite strangeness as well as isotopic spin, parity, and angular momentum. Baryon states of different strangeness are not related in any simple way; therefore, K-meson nucleon scattering amplitudes in states of different strangeness are not closely related. The

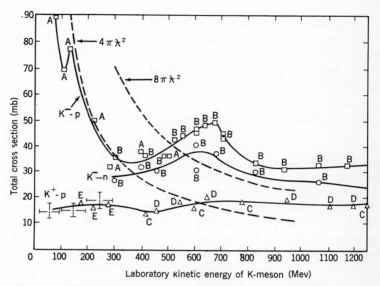

Fig. 3-6. Total cross sections for interaction between K-mesons and nucleons.[21] Measured points are labeled by: A, Berkeley bubble chamber results; B and C, recent Berkeley counter studies; D, MIT counter study; and E, earlier Berkeley counter data. The crosses indicate earlier emulsion data summarized by M. Kaplon. The dashed curves represent $4\pi\lambda^2$ and $8\pi\lambda^2$, indicating the limiting values for the production of states of spin j equal to 1/2 and 3/2, respectively.

analyses of K$^+$-p and K$^-$-n scattering, though both in pure $T = 1$ states, must be kept separate. For K$^+$-mesons on protons, only elastic scattering occurs at low energies; while the absorptive reactions K$^-$ + n → (Λ or Σ) + π are important for the $S = -1$ interaction. The energy level diagram of Figure 3-1 shows the considerable differences in available states.

The K$^+$-nucleon cross sections do not show much structure, while the K$^-$-proton cross sections show resonance type maxima at 140 and 700 Mev. It is possible that the peak near 700 Mev does not result from the existence of an isobar, but is rather a cusplike discontinuity (Section 5.8) arising from the existence of a threshold for the production of the K*, a K-π isobar. Such an explanation requires as a necessary, though not sufficient, condition that the S-wave K* production rise to nearly the limit set by the unitary character of the scattering matrix. If this is the cause, related behavior might be expected concerning the K$^+$p and K$^+$n cross sections at the same energy, as there would exist thresholds for the production of the K* with $S = +1$. Since the detailed behavior of the total cross section at a threshold depends upon the values and phases of the scattering amplitudes near that energy, values which will be quite different for K$^+$, p and K$^-$, p interactions, the anomalies may have an entirely different character. Therefore, the small anomalies in the K$^+$-p and K$^+$-n cross section rather support this unusual thesis.[22]

The low energy behavior of the K-nucleon interactions has been studied in detail.[23] The experimentally available fundamental interactions (K$^+$, p), (K$_2^0$, p), and (K$^-$, p) can be described in an especially coherent manner by an extension of the Fermi description of meson-nucleon interactions, in terms of scattering amplitudes of definite isotopic spin and angular momentum, to include strangeness as well. States $U^M_{T,S}$ are constructed where S is the strangeness number and T and M are the total isotopic spin and third component, respectively. Then we write:

$$K^+p = U^1_{1,1}$$

$$K_2^0p = \sqrt{(1/2)}\, K^0p - \sqrt{(1/2)}\, \bar{K}^0p = (1/2)U^1_{1,1}$$
$$+ (1/2)U^0_{0,1} - \sqrt{(1/2)}U^1_{1,-1} \quad (5)$$

and

$$K^-p = \sqrt{(1/2)}U^0_{1,-1} + \sqrt{(1/2)}U^0_{0,-1}$$

where the numerical coefficients are the appropriate Clebsch-Gordan coefficients connecting states of different isotopic spin representation. As a result of the interaction, each amplitude $U^M_{T,S}$, of definite isotopic spin and strangeness, is multiplied by a transition amplitude $A_{T,S}$, which, as an example, if only

S-and P-waves, and initial protons with spin $+1/2$ in the beam direction, $\uparrow$, are considered, has the usual form for the scattering of spin zero particles by spin $1/2$ particles:

$$A = k^{-1}[A_s + (2A_{p3/2} + A_{p1/2}) \cos \theta\uparrow]$$
$$+ k^{-1}[(A_{p1/2} - A_{p3/2}) \sin \theta \, e^{i\phi}\downarrow] \qquad (6)$$

where $A = i\,(1 - S)/2$, $S = \exp(2i\delta)$, or $A = \exp(i\delta) \sin \delta$. The scattered wave then has the form:

$$|K^+p\rangle \rightarrow A_{1,1}|K^+p\rangle$$

$$|K^-p\rangle \rightarrow (2)^{-1}\,(A_{1,-1} - A_{0,-1})|\bar{K}^0n\rangle$$
$$+ (2)^{-1/2}\,(A_{1,-1} + A_{0,-1})|K^-p\rangle \qquad (7)$$

or

$$|K^-p\rangle \rightarrow (2)^{-1}\,(A_{1,-1} - A_{0,-1})\,(|K_1^0n\rangle - |K_2^0n\rangle)$$
$$+ (2)^{-1/2}\,(A_{1,-1} + A_{0,-1})|K^-p\rangle$$

We analyze $(K_2^0,\ p)$ interactions into $(K^0,\ p)$, $(\bar{K}^0,\ p)$, and $(K^+,\ n)$. After evaluating and collecting coefficients of $(K^+,\ n)$, $(K_1^0,\ p)$, and $(K_2^0\ p)$, we obtain:

$$|K_2^0p\rangle \rightarrow [(4)^{-1}\,(A_{1,1} + A_{0,1}) + (2)^{-1}\,A_{1,-1}]|K_2^0p\rangle$$
$$+ [(4)^{-1}\,(A_{1,1} + A_{0,1}) - (2)^{-1}\,A_{1,-1}]|K_1^0p\rangle \qquad (8)$$
$$+ (4)^{-1}\,(2)^{1/2}\,(A_{1,1} - A_{0,1})|K^+n\rangle$$

In addition to charge exchange, characteristically proportional to the difference in the interaction of states of different isotopic spin, there is another exchange type scattering; this is the change in K-meson CP symmetry number in the transition $|K_2^0p\rangle \rightarrow |K_1^0p\rangle$, which is proportional to the difference in the amplitudes for different strangeness quantum numbers. Since the $S = 1$ and $S = -1$ interactions are quite different, the cross section for this process is large.

These reactions have been studied carefully at low energies where S-wave interactions are dominant. Angular distributions of K^+, p scattering at 225 Mev[24] suggest that the S-wave $T = 1$, $S = 1$ phase shift is negative, as would be produced by a repulsive potential. This inference is drawn because there is no evidence of the strong destructive interference between nucleonic and the repulsive coulomb scattering which should occur if the phase shift were positive, as from an attractive potential. Information concerning the $T = 0$, $S = 1$ state is less reliable as it is derived from information concerning the K^+, n interactions in complex nuclei through analyses depending upon theories of the multiple scattering of particles in nuclear matter.[25] A first approximation consists of treating the heavy nucleus as an optical medium with real and imaginary indices of refraction or real and imaginary potentials related to the real and imaginary parts of the K-nucleon forward scattering amplitudes, in a manner similar in concept to that discussed in Section 2.6. Again, the refractive and absorptive properties of the optical medium can be described in terms of a wave number $K = k_0 + i\,\kappa_0$, where $K = 2\pi A n k^{-1}$, where n is the density of nucleons in the nucleus, and A is the complex K-nucleon forward scattering amplitude at a K-nucleon center of mass momentum corresponding to k, and A is averaged over neutrons and protons. The optical potential is then $(\hbar K)^2/2m_{\rm K}$, where $m_{\rm K}$ is the K-meson mass. Measurements of the elastic scattering and charge exchange scattering of K^+-mesons from the nucleus are then used to establish the values of the K^+-nucleus potential and, from this, the real and imaginary parts of the K-nucleon forward scattering amplitudes. Total cross sections are determined from the imaginary part of the forward scattering amplitude, $Im\,A$, by use of the optical theorem $\sigma = 4\pi k^{-1}\,Im\,A$. While it is difficult to assess the validity of detailed conclusions, it appears that the K^+, n elastic scattering cross section and charge exchange cross sections are small; of the order of 10 and 5 mb, respectively, at energies near 100 Mev.[26]

Unlike the $S = 1$ low energy K-nucleon scattering, absorptive processes are important in $S = -1$ interactions. The important K^-, p reactions are $K^- + p \rightarrow \Lambda^0 + \pi^0$, $K^- + p \rightarrow \Sigma^+ + \pi^-$,

$K^- + p \rightarrow \Sigma^0 + \pi^0$, and $K^- + p \rightarrow \Sigma^- + \pi^+$. The cross sections for these are abbreviated here respectively as $\sigma(\Lambda)$, $\sigma(\Sigma^+)$, $\sigma(\Sigma^0)$, and $\sigma(\Sigma^-)$. The absorption in the $T = 0$ state will lead to an amplitude of the form $A_0[(\sqrt{1/3})\Sigma^+ - (\sqrt{1/3})\Sigma^0 + (\sqrt{1/3})\Sigma^-]$, the $T = 1$ state to $B\,\Lambda^0 + A_1\,[(\sqrt{1/2})\Sigma^+ - (\sqrt{1/2})\Sigma^-]$, where the particle symbols represent the amplitudes for those states and the numerical coefficients are again the Clebsch-Gordan coefficients connecting states of definite total isotopic spin to definite charge states of the hyperon-pion system. Since total intensities of different isotopic spin states are additive, and the Σ^0 intensity is unique to the $T = 0$ state, the absorption cross section from the $T = 0$ interaction is just $\sigma_a\,(T = 0) = 3\sigma(\Sigma^0)$. The $T = 1$ absorption cross section is given by $\sigma_a(T = 1) = \sigma(\Lambda) + \sigma(\Sigma^+) + \sigma(\Sigma^-) - 2\,\sigma(\Sigma^0)$, where we add to $\sigma(\Lambda)$ the charged sigma cross section minus the contribution to the charged sigma cross section from the $T = 0$ state (which is just twice the Σ^0 cross section). From Equation 6 (also Section 5.3), total elastic and charge exchange cross sections are written as $\sigma_{el.} = 1/4\pi k^{-2}|(1 - S_1) + (1 - S_0)|^2, \sigma_{c.e.} = 1/4\pi k^{-2}|(1 - S_1) - (1 - S_0)|^2$, where $S = \exp(2i\delta)$ and δ, the phase shift, is equal to $\alpha + i\beta$. The values of β can be determined from the values of the absorption cross sections for the two isotopic spin states: $\sigma_a(T = 0) = 1/2\pi k^{-2}(1 - |S_0|^2)$, and $\sigma_a(T = 1) = 1/2\pi k^{-2}(1 - |S_1|^2)$, where $|S_0| = \exp(-2\beta_0)$, and $|S_1| = \exp(-2\beta_1)$.

At low energy, the variation of the phase shifts with energy should be adequately described by an effective range expansion: $k \cot \delta = A^{-1} + 1/2\,Rk^2 + \cdots\cdot$ Keeping only the first term in the expansion, and writing the scattering length A as $a + ib$, we have for very low energies, where $\delta \rightarrow 0$, $a = \alpha k^{-1}$, and $b = \beta k^{-1}$: $\sigma_{el.} = \pi(a_0 + a_1)^2$, $\sigma_{c.e.} = \pi(a_0 - a_1)^2$, and $\sigma_{abs.} = 2\pi k^{-1}(b_0 + b_1)$.

Several sets of values of the four parameters can be determined from the experimental measurements of the elastic and charge exchange cross sections, and the cross sections for the various reaction channels. A more detailed analysis of the existing data leads to the conclusion that the parameters of Table 3-3 best fit the data. Solutions (a-) and (b-) are of particular interest,

Table 3-3

K$^-$-n Scattering Lengths[45]

Set	A_0, 10^{-13}cm	A_1, 10^{-13}cm
a$^+$	$0.05\pm0.2 \;+\; i(1.10\pm0.025)$	$1.45\pm0.2 \;+\; i(0.35\pm0.08)$
a$^-$	$-0.75\pm0.4 \;+\; i(2.0\pm0.35)$	$-0.85\pm0.15 + i(0.21\pm0.04)$
b$^+$	$1.25\pm0.4 \;+\; i(2.0\pm0.3)$	$0.75\pm0.2 \;+\; i(0.24\pm0.05)$
b$^-$	$-1.85\pm0.15 + i\left(1.10^{+0.9}_{-0.3}\right)$	$-0.10\pm0.2 \;+\; i(0.65\pm0.15)$
I (a$^-$, b$^+$)	$-0.22\pm1.07 + i(2.74\pm0.31)$	$0.02\pm0.33 \;+\; i(0.38\pm.08)$
II (a$^+$, b$^-$)	$-0.59\pm0.46 + i(0.96\pm0.17)$	$1.20\pm0.06 \;+\; i(0.56\pm0.15)$

as they suggest the existence of a $T = 1$ resonant state just below threshold. A negative scattering length can represent either the results of a repulsive force or of a resonance below threshold as shown in Figure 3-7. Independent of the strength of the repulsive interaction, the repulsion will not result in a value larger in magnitude than the range of forces. Therefore, a large negative scattering length suggests a resonance below threshold, and

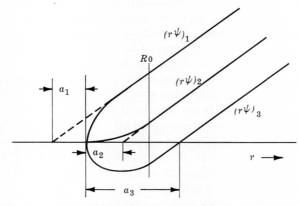

Fig. 3-7. Schematic diagram of zero energy radial wave functions for K$^-$, p scattering plotted against radius, r. A negative scattering length can result either from a repulsive force, a_2, or from a resonance below the threshold energy for K$^-$ and p at rest, a_3.

the first solution may be connected with the existence of the $T = 1$ Y*-state. If so, the Y* must have spin $1/2$ and odd parity, a result which has not been established.

The information available concerning the K^+, p and K^-, p total cross sections has been used, together with various forms of the zero momentum transfer dispersion relations in an attempt to determine the properties of contributions from the non-physical region. These contributions will result from the residues of poles representing the nonphysical reactions $K^- + p \rightarrow \Lambda^0$, and $K^- + p \rightarrow \Sigma$, as well as from the branch cut representing the reaction $K^- + p \rightarrow \Lambda + \pi$ and $\rightarrow \Sigma + \pi$, below threshold. In particular, resonances in the Λ, π scattering at total energies of 1385 and 1405 Mev may contribute almost as poles. The complexity is such as to make present results inconclusive.

The probability of capture of a K^--meson in a length of liquid hydrogen dl is equal to $n \cdot dl \cdot \sigma_a$, where n is the number of protons per cm^3, and σ_a is the absorption cross section. The probability of capture per second, ω, is $n\sigma v$, where v is the velocity, or $\omega = n \cdot 2\pi k^{-1} (b_0 + b_1) v = n \cdot 2\pi (b_0 + b_1) \hbar m^{-1}$, where m is the K-nucleon reduced mass. This capture probability is now in-dependent of energy, and the corresponding mean life ω^{-1} is about $1.5 \cdot 10^{-8}$ seconds, somewhat longer than the mean life for decay. Since nominally stopped K^--mesons are not observed to decay but interact, it is clear that they are captured in atomic orbits where the interaction probability is high. The density of protons available to a K^--meson in a $1s$ atomic state is about $[4(\pi a^3)/3]^{-1}$, where a is the meson Bohr radius. This density is about $5 \cdot 10^{31}$ protons/cm^3 or about 10^9 times as dense as liquid hydrogen. The lifetime for capture from the $1s$ state is then about $2 \cdot 10^{-17}$ seconds, which is still sufficiently long compared to the inverse of the natural frequency, $E/\hbar$, where E is the binding energy, that the state is well defined.

Capture from the $2p$ state is considerably reduced, as the meson wave function is reduced at the proton coordinate by the centrifugal barrier; however, it may still compete with radiative transitions to the $1s$ state in an isolated K^-, p atom. Since most

K-mesons are captured in high angular momentum orbits for statistical reasons, and since dipole transitions will dominate for isolated atoms, most K-mesons would end up in the p-state and p-capture might dominate. However, experiments of interest are performed in liquid hydrogen where the K-mesic atom undergoes frequent collisions with other atoms. These collisions distort the K-proton wave function, in a manner similar to the distortion induced by the Stark effect, greatly increasing the K-amplitude at the proton. This distortion can be considered as mixing s-state into the higher angular momentum states and the greatly enhanced capture results from the s-part of the wave function. As a result, it seems likely that almost all capture is from s-states.[27] This important conclusion has a number of consequences; the accurate branching ratios measured using stopped K-mesons[24] can be applied to the determination of the imaginary parts of the s-wave scattering lengths by allowing a better measurement of the ratio, and also the relative phase, of the $T = 0$, and $T = 1$, absorption amplitudes. Also, the isotropic decay distributions of the Σ and the Λ add to the evidence that the spins of these particles are $1/2$ (Section 2.3).

3.6. Strange Particle Resonances

A large number of baryon and meson states exist which decay through the strong interactions. From a phenomenological viewpoint we can consider these as resonances in the interaction of the decay products, though some of these states may be more deeply significant. Eventually, criteria may exist which will allow a differentiation between states, stable and unstable, which are in some sense fundamental and states which are dynamic in character and can be understood in terms of the interactions of the fundamental particles. To the extent of our present knowledge, these unstable states generally differ from the stable states only in energy, and energy differences in themselves need reflect only quantitative effects rather than important qualitative differences. It is then possible that a criterion

which furnishes a test of the fundamental nature of particles will
show that some of the unstable states or isobars are fundamental,
and some stable states are dynamic compounds. The dashed
lines in the energy level plots of Figure 3-1 show the positions of
the states in relation to thresholds and the masses of stable
particles while Table 3-4 lists other pertinent information concerning strange particle states.

An unstable state, like a stable state, is described first by
its symmetry properties represented by the quantum numbers
for spin, parity, strangeness, isotopic spin, and baryon number—
then by dynamic properties, resonance energy, and partial
widths for different decay modes. The resonance energy and
width can be considered as the real and imaginary parts of the
mass. In the absence of a theory of the dynamics, the identity
of the particles into which a state usually decays is not necessarily fundamental in identifying the state. An isobar such as the
Y^*, which almost always decays into a lambda and a pion, is not
necessarily more a lambda-pion state than a K-nucleon state,
a sigma-pion state or any other combination of particles which
have the requisite quantum numbers. Indeed, matrix elements
must exist which connect the Y^* with all of these states, resulting
in real transitions to those allowed energetically and virtual
transitions to those which are not.

Table 3-4

Strange Particle Resonance Parameters

Particle	Mass, Mev/c^2	Width, Mev/c^2	Isotopic spin	Spin and parity	Decay modes	Reference
K^*	885	50	1/2	$1-(?)$	(K, π)	28a
Y_1^*	1385	45	1	$(?)$	(Λ, π)	28b
					$<5\%$ (Σ, π)	
Y_0^*	1405	50	0	$(?)$	(Σ, π)	28c
	1520	16	0	$3/2-$	$(K, p)(\Sigma, \pi),$	28d
					$(\Lambda + 2\pi)$	
	1815	120	0	$\geqslant 3/2(?)$	various	28e

Certain aspects of the dynamics of these states are largely independent of any detailed understanding of the interactions and can be described in terms of resonance theory. Consider the decay of a narrow resonance or long-lived isobar, Y, at an energy E_λ, into two particles U and V. We can presume that the amplitude of the state Y will decay in time as $\exp(-t/2\tau)$, where τ is the mean life. Since time and energy are complementary, we find by a Fourier transform of the amplitude as a function of time, $A_r = \exp(-t/2\tau)\exp(-iE_\lambda t/\hbar)$; that, as a function of energy, E, the amplitude A_r is proportional to $[(E_\lambda - E) - i\Gamma/2]^{-1}$, where $\Gamma = \hbar/\tau$. As E varies from $E \ll E_\lambda$ to $E \gg E_\lambda$, the locus of the amplitude traces out a counterclockwise circle in the complex plane as shown in Figure 3-8a and the phase of the amplitude changes by 180°; the sign of the variation is determined by the sign of τ and hence causality. This basic description is modified according to the particular circumstance of the isobar production; the amplitude will be multiplied by a complex quantity representing the production amplitude for the

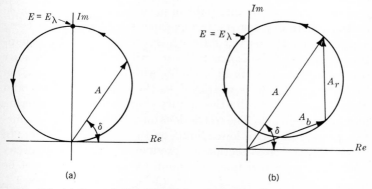

(a)   (b)

Fig. 3-8. (a) Argand diagram of the resonant scattering amplitude, A, plotted in the complex plane. As the energy, E, increases from below to above the resonant energy, E_λ; the vector representing A rotates counterclockwise. The angle is the corresponding phase shift. (b) The resonance may interfere coherently with appropriate background processes. This is represented by the addition of the amplitude A_b.

isobar, and added to a complex background amplitude, A_b, relatively independent of energy. The locus of the total amplitude, A, equal to $A_b + A_r$, will vary with energy characteristically as shown in Figure 3-8b; the resonance amplitude tracing out the circle as shown. Note that for A, the phase δ will not necessarily pass through 180°. Further, the intensity (proportional to $|A|^2$) will, in general, pass through both a maximum and a minimum, and the maximum will not necessarily occur at $E = E_\lambda$. Indeed, pathological situations may occur; the intensity may become a minimum at resonance, or even, if the center of the resonance circle should be shifted to the origin by addition of the background amplitude, the intensity will not change at all at a resonance—though the phase will.

The complication resulting from interference with background amplitudes is such as to allow the nominal measurements of such quantities as resonance energy, width, and branching ratios to differ as the state is produced under different conditions[29]; that is, at different angle and energies, or by different reactions.

Some isobars decay into pairs of particles which are available in the laboratory for scattering experiments. The scattering amplitude for the partial wave which corresponds to the quantum numbers of the isobar will vary with energy in a manner similar to that shown in Figure 3-8b, with the further restriction that the amplitude is restricted to the upper half plane and limited in magnitude by the unitary character of the scattering matrix (Section 5.2). The restrictions imposed by unitarity sometimes establish useful lower limits on the spin of the isobar. In particular, the cross section for production of an isobar decay mode b, as measured from minimum to maximum, will not be larger than: $(2j + 1) (2i + 1)^{-1} (2s + 1)^{-1} 4\pi k^{-2} (\Gamma_a \Gamma_b)^2 / \Gamma_t^2$, where j is the isobar spin, i is the spin of the incident particle a, s is the target particle spin, k the wave number in the center of mass system, Γ_a the width for the incident particle, Γ_b that for the mode b, and Γ_t the total width. The total cross section for the interaction of K^--mesons with protons near a resonance at a K^-

energy of 700 Mev is shown in Figure 3-6, together with values of $4\pi k^{-2}$, and $8\pi k^{-2}$, the limits allowed for the production of states of spin j equal to $1/2$ and $3/2$. Since the difference between maximum and minimum cross sections is larger than $4\pi k^{-2}$, the spin of the state must be greater than $1/2$.

Often, however, an isobar decays only into two particles which cannot be used for scattering experiments, such as is the case for the decay $Y^* \rightarrow \Lambda^0 + \pi$, or perhaps the isobar may decay only into three particles. The existence of such isobars and the study of their properties must then be conducted by examining the products of reactions which can produce the isobar states along with other particles. The simplest of such situations occurs when only three particles are produced. The relativistic invariant, M, formed by the sum of the four momenta of any two particles, $M^2 = (p_a + p_b)^2$, is equal to the mass of a hypothetical state which decays into those particles. A plot of probability versus this quantity can be expected to show a peak near the value of the mass of an isobar. In the same manner, the existence of isobars which decay into more than two particles can be investigated by considering the distribution of values of the invariant, M, for the several particles.

A two-dimensional representation of three body production or Dalitz-Fabri plot, discussed in detail in Section 4.2, is also very useful when the center of mass energy, W, is fixed. Here, the observed events are plotted as a function of the center of mass kinetic energies of the two particles. Figure 3-9 shows such a presentation of the data from the reaction $K^- + p \rightarrow \Lambda^0 + \pi^+ + \pi^-$, where events observed in a hydrogen bubble chamber[30] placed in a beam of 1100 Mev/c K^--mesons are plotted. Since $T + M = W - m$, where T and m are the kinetic energy and mass of a particle, a condensation or maximum in the probability of events at M equal to the mass of an isobar will be exhibited as a peak in the probability as a function of T. Such a condensation is clearly seen in Figure 3-9, where it results from the existence of a state Y^* with a mass of 1385 Mev and a width near 40 Mev. Since the isotopic spins of the Λ^0 and pion are 0 and 1, respec-

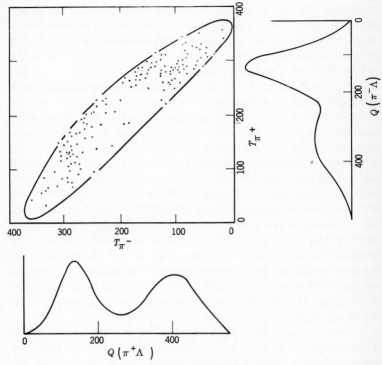

Fig. 3-9. Dalitz-Fabri plot of the final state in the process $K^- + p \to \Lambda^0 + \pi^+ + \pi^-$. Condensations along lines of $T_\pi \sim 290$ Mev correspond to the production of the Y_1^* isobar with rest energy equal to 1385 Mev.

tively, the Y* must have isotopic spin 1; the strangeness, of course, is −1.

Since equal areas of the Dalitz-Fabri plot correspond to equal volumes of phase space, deviations from a uniform population are often considered as definite indications of final state interactions. However, effects due to centrifugal barriers, symmetries, and the conservation of angular momentum, can result in large variations from a constant population.[29] The existence of peaks in the mass spectra of many particle final states which result from the existence of isobars can be described as the result of final state interactions, or the scattering of particles in the final state. Production amplitudes, considered as a function of M, with either T or W held constant, will vary generally as in Figure 3-8. Again, as the result of interference with backgrounds, measured parameters may vary considerably with the mode of production.

Methods used to measure the spins of the quasistable strange particles, the lambda, the sigma, and the K-meson, have a limited application in the determination of isobar spins. In the absence of background reactions, hyperon isobars, produced such that the component of spin in a well-defined direction z is 1/2, will decay with angular distributions determined uniquely by the spins of the isobars. In particular, spin 1/2 states will decay isotropically and spin 3/2 states should have a decay angular distribution of $1/2 + 3/2 \cos^2\theta$, where θ is the angle between the isobar decay direction and the direction of quantization z, a result discussed in more detail in Section 2.2. There are important situations in which such an alignment of the isobar will occur when the isobar is produced as a compound or intermediate state in the scattering of particles with a total spin of 1/2. Since the orbital angular momentum can contribute no component in the beam direction, the isobar will have a component of spin in the beam direction of just 1/2. As a result, the isobars Y, produced by the interaction $K^- + p \to Y \to$ (decay products) at laboratory K^- energies of 140 and 700 Mev, are aligned and will decay with angular distributions characteristic of their spin, but complicated by interference with the nonresonant background scattering.

Measurements of the elastic scattering angular distributions at the lower resonance indicate that the spin of the K^-p state at 140 Mev is 3/2, and the parity is odd.[31] The nonresonant background scattering is nearly isotropic, and neither the intensity or the angular distribution changes much as the energy is reduced. This is characteristic of s-wave scattering. Almost pure $p_{1/2}$ wave scattering would be nearly isotropic, but would depend strongly on energy at low energies. No combination of higher angular momentum waves can simulate isotropy. At the resonance, a strong $\cos^2 \theta$ component is observed (where θ is the scattering angle), while there is little, if any, evidence for other powers of $\cos \theta$, in particular, $\cos^4 \theta$ or $\cos \theta$. The presence of a $\cos^2 \theta$ term and the absence of a $\cos^4 \theta$ term immediately establishes the spin as $3/2$. A $p_{3/2}$ wave should interfere with the s-wave background to produce a fore-aft asymmetry or $\cos \theta$ term, which would change sign as the energy was varied through resonance. Since this is not observed, the resonant scattering must be in the $d_{3/2}$ state; assuming the K-meson is pseudoscalar, the state then has odd parity.

This state also decays through the Σ, π channels and analyses of the Σ angular distributions and polarizations have been used to suggest that the (NKΣ)-parity is even.[32] Below resonance the Σ, π angular distributions are nearly isotropic and, depending on the Σ-parity, are presumbly dominated by either s or $p_{1/2}$ wave production through the incident K, p s-wave channel. The resonant Σ-π state will be a $d_{3/2}$ or $p_{3/2}$ state produced through the $d_{3/2}$ K, p resonance. A good fit to the data was found for an s-d combination ψ which would require a positive parity for the Σ, assuming the usual conventions and odd K-parity (Section 3.7). Minami type ambiguities can be excluded. The regular Minami transpose $\bar{\sigma} \cdot \bar{\theta} | \psi \rangle$ (Section 2.3), which has the opposite parity, but the same angular distributions, is excluded as it predicts the opposite signs of polarization since the operator $\bar{\sigma} \cdot \bar{\theta}$, where $\bar{\sigma}$ is the Dirac spin operator, rotates the spin $180°$ about the production direction θ. Since the polarization depends upon terms like $2Im \, A^* B$ where A and B are nonspin-flip and spin-flip amplitudes, complex conjugation, which changes the signs of the phases of the amplitudes, changes the signs of the polarizations; therefore, $(\bar{\sigma} \cdot \bar{\theta} | \psi \rangle)^*$ leads to the same angular distributions and polarizations and is a solution of the opposite parity. Complex conjugation, however, is essentially time reversal. The resonant amplitude for this negative sigma-parity solution $(\bar{\sigma} \cdot \bar{\theta} | \psi \rangle)^*$ will now violate causality by moving clockwise, with energy, in the complex plane instead of counterclockwise which is required if the decay is to take place after the state is formed.

The validity of this conclusion, that the Σ-parity is even, is limited by the existence of unrelated odd parity solutions which may not be excluded by the data.

Hyperon isobars produced as final state interactions are aligned in certain circumstances. In reactions of the type, $K^- + p \rightarrow Y^* + \pi^-$, if the total spin of the initial particles, in this case, the K^- and proton, is $1/2$, and if the spin of the extra particle, here the π^-, is zero, Y^* produced in the forward or backward direction will be aligned such that the component of Y^* spin in the beam direction is only $1/2$. The arguments are similar to those used to determine the hyperon spins, as discussed in Section 2.3. At certain energies and angles of production, the isobar may be polarized. An analysis of the correlation between the isobar polarization direction and the polarization of the hyperon into which it decays will then establish the parity of the isobar. Again, this is discussed in detail in Section 4.3 in reference to the parity of final states of hyperons decaying by weak interactions. Results of a straightforward application of these methods imply that the spin of the Y^* is $1/2$, that the decay is to an s-wave Λ^0-π system, and that the parity is then odd.[33] The reliability of these conclusions is marred considerably by difficulties resulting from coherent interference with non-resonant processes. A small intensity of such states can radically modify decay angular distributions and affect the determination of the Y^* spin, parity, widths, and branching ratios to the $\Sigma + \pi$ mode.[34] Interferences can complicate the analysis of scattering experiments in much the same manner.

A natural unit of isobar lifetime τ is provided by the quantity a/v, where a is the radius of the elementary particle and v is the relative velocity of the decay particles. The existence of centrifugal barriers will lengthen the lifetime by a factor P^{-1}, where P is called the penetration factor, and the intrinsic probability of decay, called here θ^2, the reduced width, may be less than 1. If we use as a radius $a = \hbar/m_\pi c$, we have for the width of the state $\Gamma = \hbar/\tau = \theta^2 (m_\pi c^2) \cdot \beta \cdot P$ or the sum of these quantities for various decay modes. For most isobars, it appears that $\Sigma_i \theta_i^2$ for all decay modes is not very different from 1, or about the same as that for decay from a square well, suggesting that such isobars may represent simple configurations.

Emphasis has been placed on the importance of establishing the patterns of isobars as an aid to insights into symmetries. In connection with this, one must consider classes of states which may be difficult to observe. Specific examples are interesting. Consider, for example, a search for a hypothetical isobar Y by measurements of total and partial cross sections for the K$^-$-nucleon interaction. The cross sections for a process vary with energy E at high energies as E^{-2}, with isobar spin as $(2j + 1)$, and are further proportional to $\Gamma_s \Gamma_a / (\Gamma_s + \Gamma_a)$, where Γ_s is the elastic scattering width and Γ_a is the width for all other processes. The existence of the state will be obscured if the spin j is small, if E is large, and if $\Gamma_s \ll \Gamma_a$. If the width Γ_a is large, any variations which do occur near the resonance energy may be obscured by variations in nonresonant cross sections. Such a state might be better seen in a final state interaction although it also might be obscured there. States with large values of isotopic spin are difficult to detect. Consider for definiteness a hyperon isobar with $S = -1$ and $T = 3$. It can decay to $\Lambda + \pi$, K + n, or $\Sigma + \pi$ only through the breakdowns in the conservation of isotopic spin to be expected through electromagnetic effects manifested primarily in the mass difference between members of isotopic spin multiplets. If the mass is less than that of a sigma plus two pions, the state will be quite narrow, perhaps 1 Mev or less. In final state interactions it will be detectable as an isotopic spin violating two body breakup of the $T = 3$ state, produced in reactions such as $\pi^- + p \rightarrow Y + \pi + \pi$. If the mass is larger, peaks in the invariant mass M for the sigma and two pions produced in such reactions as $\pi^- + p \rightarrow \Sigma + 4\pi$, may reveal the existence of the state.

Figure 3-1 shows what appears to be an unusual degree of correlation between resonances and thresholds, which has led to several conjectures concerning possible relationships—notably that some of the peaks are not resonances, but cusplike anomalies related to the existence of thresholds, very much as discussed in Section 5.7. Such an explanation requires as a necessary, though not sufficient, condition that the threshold reaction rise with increasing energy to large values very quickly; values near the limits imposed by the unitary condition. Two particular situations where cross section peaks may result from cusps rather than from resonances have been mentioned; notably, the peak in the K^-, p total cross section near 700 Mev (Section 3.5), and the peak in the cross section for the process $\pi^- + p \rightarrow \Lambda + K$ at 900 Mev pion energy (Section 3.3).

Another mechanism, which may be important and may produce cross section peaks which are not truly resonances, involves the scattering of an isobar by one of its decay products.[35] In order to illustrate this type of interaction, let us consider the scattering of a pion by an isobar Y which decays into a lambda and a pion. In particular, consider the scattering of the pion by a Y target such that the Y decays into a lambda and a pion, and the incoming pion then interacts with the lambda to form a Y as shown in Figure 3-10a. Kinematically, this is elastic π, Y scattering. The angle of decay, ϕ, of the target Y is the laboratory scattering angle; for each value of ϕ, the incoming pion energy required for resonant interaction to form a Y will be

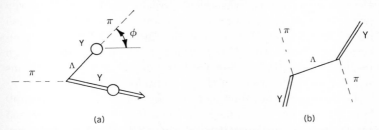

Fig. 3-10. (a) Diagram illustrating the physical scattering on an isobar, Y, by one of its decay products. Kinematically, this is elastic π, Y scattering. (b) Exchange scattering diagram. The vertices represent decays, corresponding to the hypothesis that $M_Y > (M_\Lambda + M_\pi)$.

different. The scattering of pions will be enhanced over this physically limited range of energies.

This effect is not limited to physical situations. In the language of dispersion relations we consider Figure 3-10b. For any fixed value of the momentum transfer invariant $(p_Y + p_{\pi'})^2$, where the p represent four momenta, the scattering amplitude will have a pole in the physical region of the total energy invariant, $(p_\pi + p_Y)^2$. The existence of this pole enhances scattering cross sections over a range of total energies. Since the process $\pi + Y \rightarrow \pi + Y$ is linked to more observable reactions such as $K + p \rightarrow \pi + Y$, and hence to $K + p \rightarrow K + p$, etc., a peak may be produced in many processes even as the result of a single resonance. This peak will differ from resonances, as described earlier in this section, both in shape and in the involvement of a mixture of different states of parity and angular momentum.

3.7. Hypernuclei

Conservation of strangeness restricts the low energy interaction of lambda-hyperons and nucleons to elastic scattering. If the interaction is primarily attractive, bound states of nucleons plus a lambda should exist with a lifetime of the magnitude of the lifetime of the lambda. Such hypernuclei were indeed discovered by Danysz and his collaborators[36] as spallation products or hyperfragments resulting from high energy particles from the cosmic radiation interacting with emulsion nuclei. Studies of these assemblies provide information concerning both the strong interactions of the lambda and nucleon responsible for the lambda binding and the weak interactions which lead to the decay of the hyperfragment.

To the extent that nuclear forces are charge independent and spin independent, the energy of nuclear states will be ordered by symmetry considerations; states with highest symmetries, and correspondingly fewest nodes in the space wave functions, will have the lowest energies. Each space wave function will be associated with different spin and charge states. Degeneracies of these supermultiplets are removed by the well-known spin dependences of nuclear forces and by electromagnetic interactions. In light nuclei, these interactions are not strong enough to break down the ordering of the lowest energy levels. If lambda-nucleon forces are not both very strong and very strongly spin or charge dependent, a similar supermultiplet structure should be obtained for light hypernuclei. Since, of course, the Pauli principle does not operate between the lambda and the nucleons, the single lambda will lie in an s-state with respect to a nucleon structure not radically different from a state of the parent nucleus. Furthermore, the lowest state of the hypernuclei will be the equivalent of a lambda plus the ground state of the parent nucleus—though if the first excited state lies very close to the ground state, it is conceivable that these could be reversed in the hypernucleus.

Since the weak interaction responsible for the hypernucleus decay allows a lifetime of the order of 10^{13} times characteristic nuclear times, hypernucleus states are well defined. Such lifetimes are longer than most nuclear electromagnetic transition times, so the state which decays by emission of nucleons and perhaps a pion will almost surely represent the hypernucleus ground state. According to the arguments above, the spin of this state will be equal to the spin of the parent nucleus plus or minus $1/2$, and, since the isotopic spin of the Λ is 0, the isotopic spin of the hypernucleus will be the same as that of the parent nucleus.

The conventional symbol for a hypernucleus is $_\Lambda X^A$ where X is the chemical symbol representing the parent nucleus, and A is the total number of baryons. This somewhat misleading convention (for example, $_\Lambda He^4$ is essentially He^3 plus a Λ and not necessarily much like He^4) arose historically largely because the Λ^0 was considered, inaccurately, to take the place of a neutron in a nucleus.

Nuclear matter has approximately constant density and the radii of nuclei can be described by the relationship $R = 1.1 \cdot 10^{-13} A^{1/3}$, where A is the number of nucleons and the parameter 1.1 is largely derived from electron scattering experiments.[37] The potential seen by the lambda can be expected to be proportional to the density of nuclear matter and the lambda wave function will then have the characteristic form appropriate to a particle in a square well: $r\psi = A \sin Kr$; $r < R$: $r\psi = B \exp(-\kappa r)$; $r > R$ where $K = \pm \{2m\hbar^{-2}(V_0 - |E|)\}^{1/2}$, and $\kappa = \pm (2m|E|\hbar^{-2})^{1/2}$, where E is the binding energy and V_0 the potential depth. A bound state will exist at an energy E such that $KR \cot KR = -\kappa R$. The curve shown in Figure 3-11 shows the binding energy plotted as a function of A, for a well depth chosen as 18.5 Mev, weaker than a well depth appropriate for nucleons (≈ 60 Mev). The close fit of the experimental measurements attests to the validity of this simple picture.

If a parent nucleus X^A is not stable against decay by heavy particle emission by an energy ΔE, the corresponding hypernucleus $_\Lambda X^{A+1}$ will also be unstable unless the Λ^0 binding energy is greater than ΔE. Except for Be^8, this energy difference* for light unstable nuclei is larger than the Λ^0 binding energy; so, with the exception of $_\Lambda Be^9$, hypernuclei are not formed from unstable light nuclei. Table 3-5 shows[38] the known light hypernuclei together with the Λ^0 binding energy, the parent nuclei and the isotopic spin. States enclosed by parentheses represent nuclear states which are unstable or hypernuclei which have not been observed. The presence or absence of various hypernuclei is in accord with the assumptions which were made. Furthermore, the similar binding energies of mirror hypernuclei establishes charge symmetry of the lambda-nucleon forces; that is, lambda-neutron and lambda-proton forces are nearly the same.

Deviations from the square well curve of Figure 3-11 occur which are related to inadequacies of the approximations which were made. Important deviations will occur resulting from varia-

---

* This is not to be confused with the resonance energy; e.g., the $He^4 + n$ scattering resonance corresponding to the ground state of He^5 occurs at an energy of about 0.8 Mev, however, the interaction must be increased by very much more than 0.8 Mev to bind the neutron and form a stable He^5.

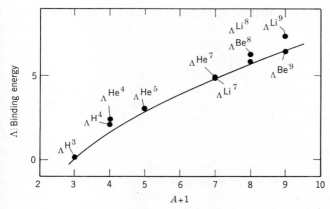

Fig. 3-11. Binding energy in Mev of the Λ^0 in various light hypernuclei as a function of their atomic number, A. The curve is based on a square potential well; radius $= (1.1 \cdot A^{1/3} + 0.5) \cdot 10^{-13}$ cm, depth $= 18.5$ Mev. The 0.5 represents an estimate of the Λ^0-nucleon interaction radius.

tions in nuclear density and from the spin dependence of the lambda-nucleon forces. Analyses of differences between the binding energies of $_\Lambda He^4$ and $_\Lambda He^5$ by Dalitz and his collaborators, have resulted in the conclusion that lambda-nucleon forces are

Table 3-5

Light Hypernuclei

A	I	Parent	Hypernucleus	Binding energy, Mev
1	1/2	(n), (p)	$(_\Lambda n^2)$, $(_\Lambda H^2)$	—,—
2	0	H^2	$_\Lambda H^3$	0.2
2	1	(nn), (np), (He^2)	$(_\Lambda n^3)$, —, $(_\Lambda He^3)$	—,—,—
3	1/2	H^3, He^3	$_\Lambda H^4$, $_\Lambda He^4$	1.81, 1.94
4	0	He^4	$_\Lambda He^5$	2.82
5	1/2	(He^5), (Li^5)	$(_\Lambda He^6)$, $(_\Lambda Li^6)$	—,—
6	0	Li^6	$_\Lambda Li^7$	4.80
6	1	(Be^6), —, He^6	$_\Lambda Be^7$,—,$_\Lambda He^7$	3.7, 4.9
7	1/2	Be^7, Li^7	$_\Lambda Be^8$, $_\Lambda Li^8$	6.25, 5.6
8	0	(Be^8)	$_\Lambda Be^9$	6.43

strongly spin dependent[39] and, less certainly, that forces in the
singlet state are larger than in the triplet state.[40] A reasonable
measure of the average interaction between the lambda and the
nucleus is the quantity $A^{-1} \int V \, d\tau$, where V is the lambda
nucleus potential and the integration is taken over the volume
of the parent nucleus as determined by electron scattering experiments on the nucleus, augmented by calculations of the
compressive change in size induced by the presence of the
lambda. In the absence of spin dependent forces, the value of V,
adjusted to fit the experimentally observed binding energies,
should be constant. Actual binding energies are such that the
required value of the average potential for $_\Lambda He^4$ is much greater
than for $_\Lambda He^5$. Since He^4 is symmetric, the interaction of the
bound lambda in $_\Lambda He^5$ is averaged over lambda-nucleon spin
states; the lambda bound to He^3 may be preferentially aligned or
antialigned to the excess spin of He^3 according to whether
triplet or singles forces are greater, and the average interactions
of the most strongly bound state, characterized by the integral
introduced, will be greater than for $_\Lambda He^5$.

Approximately 67% of $_\Lambda He^4$ hypernuclei decay[41] by the transition $_\Lambda He^4 \rightarrow He^4 + \pi^0$, where the nucleon from the lambda decay
is captured into the vacant s-state of the alpha particle. If the
spin of $_\Lambda He^4$ is 0, the pion must be in an s-state and only s-wave
lambda decays will contribute to the reaction. If the spin of
$_\Lambda He^4$ is 1, the pion must be in a p-state, the final state will have
even parity, and only p-state lambda decays will contribute.
s-wave decay of the lambda is more important (Section 4.3),
so the large ratio of mesonic to nonmesonic decay observed experimentally suggests that the spin of the $_\Lambda He^4$ is zero, and that
singlet state lambda-nucleon forces are stronger than triplet
forces.

If the $_\Lambda He^4$ spin is zero, the existence of the reaction $K^- +$
$He^4 \rightarrow {}_\Lambda He^4 + \pi^-$ shows that the $(nK\Lambda)$ parity is odd.[42] This
reaction occurs in about 3% of the interactions of stopped K^--
mesons in liquid helium.[43] Since the intrinsic spins of all of the
particles are 0, the orbital angular momentum of the initial

K,He^4 system must be the same as that of the final π, $_\Lambda$He^4 system. The product of the intrinsic parties of the initial state particles and final state particles must then be the same. Taking the lambda and nucleon parities to be even, the He^4 and $_\Lambda$He^4 must be even and the K parity must be the same as the pion parity, which is odd.

Conservation of strangeness and of isotopic spin restrict the virtual transitions which contribute to lambda-nucleon forces. In particular, no single pion exchange is possible and the longest range forces will be the result of the exchange of two pions or the exchange of one K-meson, according to parts a and b of Figure 3-12. It may be the shorter range of the interaction, rather than a difference in coupling strengths, which leads to the lambda-nucleon interaction being weaker than the nucleon-nucleon interaction. Nucleon-sigma forces may be larger, however, since single pion exchange can contribute, as part c, Figure 3-12 shows. The binding energy curves of Figure 3-11, which suggest that $_\Lambda$H^2 does not exist, does not preclude the existence of a hypernucleus (Σ^+, p) or (Σ^-, n); however, there is little experimental evidence for such compounds. It is also conceivable that (K$^+$, nucleus) compounds exist.

Hypernuclei decays are experimentally separated into mesonic and nonmesonic decays. Nonmesonic decays occur by two mechanisms: the real pion emitted in lambda decay interacts with two nucleons and is absorbed, the nucleons carrying off the energy; and more important, virtual, stimulated, transitions such as those represented by parts d and e of Figure 3-12 occur. The probability of nonmesonic decays will be greater in heavy nuclei than in the lightest nuclei, primarily because the greater lambda binding energy restricts the lambda wave function strongly to the region of nuclear matter, thereby increasing the probability of the stimulated nonmesonic decays. On the other hand, mesonic decays are restricted by the Pauli principle. Nucleons from a free lambda decay have a momentum of only 100 Mev/c, far below the top of the Fermi sea in the nucleus. There is then little phase space available for the decay.

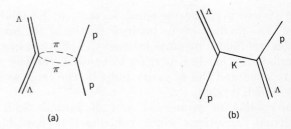

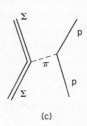

Fig. 3-12. (a), (b), and (c), Feynman diagrams representing virtual transitions which contribute to lambda-nucleon forces; (d) and (e), diagrams representing virtual transitions which lead to nonmesonic decay of hypernuclei.

Mesonic decay in light nuclei is not much restricted by either the Pauli principle or the reabsorption of the pion by the remaining nucleus. A quantitative investigation of the decay modes directed towards connecting results in hypernuclei decay with information on free decay is then possible. Nonmesonic decay, as illustrated in parts d and e of Figure 3-12, is related to the mesonic decay very much as internal conversion is related to nuclear electromagnetic transitions. Nucleons, coupled to the lambda through their pion field, provide a channel of de-excitation for hypernuclei, even as orbital electrons provide such a channel for nuclear electromagnetic decay by means of the direct coulomb coupling of the electrons to the excited nucleus. Even as the electromagnetic conversion coefficient is strongly dependent upon the spin change, the nonmesonic decay to mesonic decay ratio will be spin dependent. The mesonic decay transition probably will be proportional to the square of a coupling constant, representing the strength of the weak interaction coupling the lambda to the pion and nucleon, times the intensity at the origin of the appropriate part of the pion-nucleon plane wave, so that the transition probability will be proportional to $k^{2l+1}/(2l + 1)!!^2$, where k is the relevant wave number and l is the orbital angular momentum. For the mesonic decay mode, the pion momentum is about 100 Mev/c; for the nonmesonic decay, $n + \Lambda \rightarrow n + n$, the final state, center of mass momentum is about 400 Mev/c. The ratio of nonmesonic to mesonic transition probabilities will be $K \cdot (400/100)^{2l+1} \approx (16)^l$, where K is a constant for esch nucleus, determined from the considerations stated above. Since the dependence upon l is so strong, analyses of decay ratios in light hypernuclei[44] have contributed to the determination of the angular momentum of the products of lambda decay and hence the lambda spin. In this manner, an interpretation of the experimental results that the pion mode is important in the decay of light hyperfragments is in agreement with the conclusion that the lambda decays predominantly to s-wave states.

REFERENCES

1. R. Kronig, *J. Opt. Soc. Am.*, **12**, 547 (1926); H. A. Kramers, *Atti. Congr. Intern. Fisici, Como*, **2**, 545 (1927).
2. M. Gell-Mann, *Phys. Rev.*, **106**, 1296 (1957); J. S. Schwinger, *Ann. Phys.*, **2**, 407 (1957).
3. Dynamic consequences of global symmetry have been studied extensively by A. Pais, *Phys. Rev.*, **110**, 574 (1958).
4. M. L. Goldberger, *Phys. Rev.*, **99**, 979 (1955); M. L. Goldberger, H. Miyazawa, and R. Oehme, *Phys. Rev.*, **99**, 986 (1955); an excellent introductory review is provided by J. D. Jackson in G. R. Screaton, ed., *Dispersion Relations*, Oliver and Boyd, Edinburgh, 1960.
5. S. Mandelstam, *Phys. Rev.*, **112**, 1344 (1958); especially valuable reviews have been prepared by G. F. Chew, *Ann. Rev., Nucl. Sci.*, **9**, 29 (1959); Annual Reviews, Palo Alto, 1959, and in G. R. Screaton, ed., *Dispersion Relations*, Oliver and Boyd, Edinburgh, 1960.
6. G. F. Chew and F. E. Low, *Phys. Rev.*, **113**, 1640 (1959).
7. F. Eisler, R. Plano, A. Prodell, N. Samios, M. Schwartz, J. Steinberger, P. Bassi, V. Borelli, G. Puppi, H. Tanaka, P. Waloschek, V. Zoboli, M. Conversi, P. Franzini, L. Mannelli, R. Santangelo, and V. Silvestrini, *Nuovo Cimento*, **10**, 468 (1958); S. E. Wolf, N. Schmitz, L. Lloyd, W. Laskar, F. Crawford, Jr., J. Button, J. Anderson, and G. Alexander, *Rev. Mod. Phys.*, **33**, 439 (1961); C. Baltay, H. Courant, W. Fickinger, E. Fowler, H. Kraybill, J. Sandweiss, J. Sanford, D. Stonehill, and H. Taft, *Rev. Mod. Phys.*, **33**, 374 (1961); also, private communications from N. Samios and F. Eisler, Brookhaven National Laboratory, Upton, New York.
8. The height of the peak above background is about 23 mb; H. C. Burrowes, D. O. Caldwell, D. H. Frisch, D. A. Hill, D. M. Ritson, R. A. Schluter, and M. A. Wahlig, *Phys. Rev. Letters*, **2**, 119 (1959); J. C. Brisson, J. Detoef, P. Falk-Vairant, L. van Rossum, G. Valladas, and L. C. L. Yuan, *Phys. Rev. Letters*, **3**, 561 (1959); this is larger than $(16/3) \pi K^{-2}$, the maximum for a $T = 1/2, J = 3/2$ state (Section 3.6).
9. R. K. Adair, *Phys. Rev.*, **111**, 632 (1958); A. N. Baz and L. B. Okun, *Soviet Phys. JETP (English Transl.)*, **8**, 526 (1959).
10. J. Sakurai, *Phys. Rev.*, **107**, 908 (1957).
11. L. Michel and H. Rouhaninejad, *Phys. Rev.*, **122**, 242 (1961).
12. P. Cziffra, M. MacGregor, M. Moravcsik, and H. Stapp, *Phys. Rev.*, **114**, 880 (1959).
13. G. Breit and M. H. Hull, Jr., *Nucl. Phys.*, **15**, 216 (1960).
14. R. I. Loutitt, T. W. Morris, D. C. Rahm, R. R. Rau, A. M Thorndike, W. J. Willis, and R. M. Lea, *Phys. Rev.*, **123**, 1465 (1961).

15. E. Ferrari, *Nuovo Cimento*, 15, 652 (1960), and *Phys. Rev.*, 120, 988 (1960).
16. H. Brown, B. Culwick, W. B. Fowler, M. Gailloud, T. Kalogeropoulous, J. Kopp, R. Lea, R. Louttit, T. Morris, R. Shutt, A. Thorndike, M. Webster, C. Baltay, E. Fowler, J. Sandweiss, J. Sanford, and H. Taft, *Phys. Rev. Letters*, 8, 255 (1962); and a joint publication by the CERN laboratory, Ecole Polytechnique, and the Saclay laboratory, *Phys. Rev. Letters*, 8, 257 (1962).
17. B. McDaniel, A. Silverman, R. Wilson, and G. Cortellessa, *Phys. Rev. Letters*, 1, 108 (1958), and *Phys. Rev.*, 115, 1039 (1959); P. L. Donoho and R. L. Walker, *Phys. Rev.*, 112, 981 (1958); D. Edwards, R. Anderson, F. Turkot, and W. Woodward, *Proceedings of the 1960 International Conference on High Energy Physics at Rochester*, Interscience, 1960, p. 369.
18. N. Kroll and M. Ruderman, *Phys. Rev.*, 93, 223 (1954).
19. R. H. Capps, *Phys. Rev.*, 114, 920 (1959); M. Kawaguchi and M. J. Moravcsik, *Phys. Rev.*, 107, 563 (1957); A. Fujii and R. E. Marshak, *Phys. Rev.*, 107, 570 (1957).
20. M. J. Moravcsik, *Phys. Rev. Letters*, 2, 352 (1959).
21. M. Ferro-Luzzi, R. D. Tripp, and M. B. Watson, *Phys. Rev. Letters*, 8, 28 (1962); V. Cook, D. Keefe, L. T. Kerth, P. G. Murphy, W. A. Wenzel, and T. F. Zipf, *Phys. Rev. Letters*, 7, 182 (1961), a comprehensive list of references to K^+ cross section work is presented here; L. T. Kerth, *Rev. Mod. Phys.*, 3, 389 (1961).
22. J. S. Ball and W. R. Frazer, *Phys. Rev. Letters*, 7, 204 (1961). The general character of these results depends less on the specific calculation than on the rapid rise in K^* production itself.
23. R. Ross and W. E. Humphrey, reported by L. Alvarez, reported in *Proc. of the Ninth Intern. Ann. Conf. on High Energy Physics*, Academy of Sciences, U.S.S.R. (1960); K_2^0 interactions are measured by D. Luers, I. Mittra, S. Yamamoto, and W. Willis, *Phys. Rev. Letters*, 7, 255 (1961).
24. Reported by L. Alvarez, *Proc. of the Ninth Intern. Ann. Conf. on High Energy Physics*, Academy of Sciences, U. S. S. R. (1960).
25. K. M. Watson, *Rev. Mod. Phys.*, 30, 565 (1958).
26. D. Fournet-Davis, N. Kwak, and M. F. Kaplon, *Phys. Rev.*, 117, 846 (1960).
27. This effect was first noted by L. Madansky; a detailed discussion is presented by T. B. Day, G. A. Snow, and J. Sucher, *Phys. Rev. Letters*, 3, 61 (1959).
28. (a) M. H. Alston, L. W. Alvarez, P. Eberhard, M. L. Good, W. Graziano, H. K. Ticho, and S. G. Wojcicki, *Phys. Rev. Letters*, 6, 300 (1961).

   (b) M. H. Alston, L. W. Alvarez, P. Eberhard, M. Good, W. Graziano,
       H. K. Ticho, and S. G. Wojcicki, *Phys. Rev. Letters*, 5, 520 (1960);
       H. Martin, L. Leipuner, W. Chinowski, F. Shively, and R. Adair.
       Phys. Rev, Letters, 6, 283 (1961); J. Berge, P. Bastien, O. Dahl, M.
       Ferro-Luzzi, J. Kirz, D. H. Miller, J. J. Murray, A. H. Rosenfeld,
       R. D. Tripp, and M. B. Watson, *Phys. Rev. Letters*, 6, 597 (1961).
   (c) There is still some uncertainty concerning the existence of this
       state. M. H. Alston, L. W. Alvarez, P. Eberhard, M. L. Good, W.
       Graziano, H. K. Ticho, and S. G. Wojcicki, *Phys. Rev. Letters*, 6,
       698 (1961).
   (d) M. Ferro-Luzzi, R. D. Tripp, and M. B. Watson, *Phys. Rev. Letters*,
       8, 28 (1962).
   (e) L. T. Kerth, *Rev. Mod. Phys.*, 33, 389 (1961).
29. R. K. Adair, *Rev. Mod. Phys.*, 33, 406 (1961).
30. M. Alston, L. W. Alvarez, P. Eberhard, M. L. Good, W. Graziano,
    H. K. Ticho, and S. G. Wojcicki, *Phys. Rev. Letters*, 5, 520 (1960).
31. M. Ferro-Luzzi, R. D. Tripp, and M. B. Watson, *Phys. Rev. Letters*, 8,
    28 (1962).
32. R. D. Tripp, M. B. Watson, and M. Ferro-Luzzi, *Phys. Rev. Letters*, 8,
    175 (1962).
33. H. Martin, L. Leipuner, W. Chinowski, F. Shively, and R. Adair,
    Phys. Rev. Letters, 6, 283 (1961); J. Berge, P. Bastien, O. Dahl, M.
    Ferro-Luzzi, J. Kirz, D. H. Miller, J. J. Murray, A. H. Rosenfeld,
    R. D. Tripp, and M. B. Watson, *Phys. Rev. Letters*, 6, 597 (1961).
34. A particularly interesting example of the effects of interference are
    shown by R. H. Dalitz and D. H. Miller, *Phys. Rev. Letters*, 6, 562
    (1961). They consider the interference resulting from the resonant
    scattering of two pions by the lambda in the reaction $K^- + p \rightarrow$
    $\Lambda + \pi + \pi$.
35. M. Nauenberg and A. Pais, *Phys. Rev. Letters*, 8, 82 (1962); R. F.
    Peierls, *Phys. Rev. Letters*, 6, 641 (1961).
36. M. Danysz and J. Pniewski, *Phil. Mag.*, 44, 348 (1953).
37. R. Hofstadter, *Ann. Rev. Nucl. Sci.*, 7, 231 (1957).
38. R. G. Ammar, R. Levi-Setti, W. E. Slater, S. Limentani, P. E. Schlein,
    and P. H. Steinberg, *Nuovo Cimento.* 15, 181 (1960); R. Levi-Setti,
    W. E. Slater, and V. L. Telegdi, *Nuovo Cimento*, 10, 68 (1958).
39. R. H. Dalitz and B. W. Downs, *Phys. Rev.*, 111, 967 (1958); *Phys. Rev.*,
    114, 593 (1959).
40. R. H. Dalitz and L. Liu, *Phys. Rev.*, 116, 1312 (1959).
41. R. C. Ammar, R. Levi-Setti, W. E. Slater, S. Limentani, P. E. Schlein,
    and P. H. Steinberg, *Nuovo Cimento*, 19, 20 (1961).
42. R. H. Dalitz, *Proceedings of the Sixth Annual Rochester Conference on
    High Energy Physics*, Interscience, New York, 1956.

43. M. M. Block, E. B. Brucker, I. S. Hughes, T. K. Kuchi, C. Meltzer, F. Anderson, A. Pevsner, E. M. Harth, J. Leitner, and H. O. Cohn, *Phys. Rev. Letters*, **3**, 291 (1959).

44. R. Karplus and M. Ruderman, *Phys. Rev.* **102**, 247 (1956).

45. Solutions, a⁺, a⁻, b⁺, b⁻, are from R. H. Dalitz, *Rev. Mod. Phys.*, **33**, 471 (1962); also, R. H. Dalitz and S. F. Tuan, *Ann. Phys. (N. Y.)*, **8**, 100 (1959); a chi-square analysis by R. Ross and W. Humphrey show minima representing Solutions I and II, presented by R. Dalitz, *Proc. Aix-en-Provence Intern. Conf. on Elementary Particles, September, 1962*. Interpretation by R. H. Capps and R. L. Schult, *Phys. Rev.*, **122**, 1659 (1961), of K⁻, D cross sections; L. Alvarez, *Proc. of the Ninth Intern. Ann. Conf. on High Energy Physics*, Academy of Sciences, U.S.S.R. (1960); analyses of low-energy K⁻ interactions in emulsion, W. Alles, N. Biswas, M. Ceccarelli, and J. Crussard, *Nuovo Cimento*, **6**, 571 (1957); R. D. Hill, J. Heatherington, and D. G. Ravenhall, *Phys. Rev.*, **122**, 267 (1961), favor solutions such as Solution I.

CHAPTER 4

Weak Interactions

4.1. General Considerations

The recent history of the study of the weak interactions is a history of the endeavor to understand all weak interactions from a unified viewpoint—the universal Fermi interaction, or UFI. At the present time, there has been considerable success in accounting for many properties of the weak interactions of non-strange particles by a description in terms of the coupling of four fermions through an interaction described compactly in terms of the Lagrangian density as[1]:

$$L = G\, j\, j^* + \text{Hermitian conjugate} \tag{1}$$

The charged current j has the form $j = j_e + j_\mu + j_n$ where $j_e = \bar{\psi}_e \gamma_\mu (1 + \gamma_5)\psi_\nu$ and $j_\mu = \bar{\psi}_\mu \gamma_\mu (1 + \gamma_5)\psi_{\nu'}$ are lepton current terms, and j_n is a baryon current term, typically: $j_n = \bar{\psi}_n \gamma_\mu (1 + \gamma_5)\psi_p$; where the barred and unbarred quantities represent particle creation and annihilation operators and the γ's are the Dirac operators. The neutrino associated with the μ-decay carries a prime, in recognition that it differs from the β-decay neutrino.

There is considerable experimental evidence for the validity of this statement of the interaction, inasmuch as it represents specific decays, such as β-decay. Since $\bar{\psi}\gamma_\mu\psi$ and $\bar{\psi}i\gamma_\mu\gamma_5\psi$ transform as a vector, V, and axial vector, A, respectively, the interaction is a $V - A$ interaction.[1,2] The A part appears to be about 20% stronger for nucleon decays, a fact which may result from meson current effects. The evidence for the complete description is much less definite, and relation 1 must be considered as an attractive speculation. The consequences of relation 1 are summarized in the Puppi[3] triangles of Figure 4-1. According to this scheme, first order transitions take place only between fermion pairs at vertices connected by the sides of the triangle. It is permissable to move a particle from incident to final state, or vice versa, changing it from a particle to antiparticle. We then have as allowed transitions in this description, the well-known decays: $n \rightarrow e^- + p + \bar{\nu}$, $\mu^\pm \rightarrow e^\pm + \nu + \bar{\nu}'$, etc. Furthermore, leptons are conserved, and in addition, the reaction $\mu^\pm \rightarrow e^\pm + e^+ + e^-$ is forbidden, all in accord with experiment. Pion decay takes place through formation of virtual baryon pairs: $\pi^+ \rightarrow p + \bar{n} \rightarrow \mu^+ + \nu'$. Of course, this schematic description is useful inasmuch as it is a compact and correct representation of experimental results. To that extent, it must be contained in a more fundamental view, such as the hypothesis that all

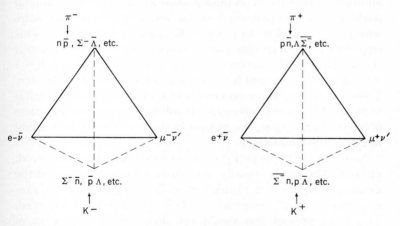

Fig. 4-1. The Puppi triangles representing the universal Fermi interaction. It is assumed that first order transitions take place only between pairs of fermions at vertices connected by a side of one of the triangles. The upper vertices represent baryon pairs which can annihilate virtually to produce a π^+ or π^-; similarly, the lower represent K^+ or K^-.

weak interactions take place through an intermediate charged vector boson.

Strangeness changing transitions are obtained by adding a strangeness changing current j_s to j in (1), where j_s changes the strangeness by 1. Typically, j_s has a form such as $j_s = \bar{\psi}_\Lambda \gamma_\mu (1 + \gamma_5)\psi_p$, where the strangeness of the lambda plus antiproton is equal to their charge. The absence of decays such as $\Xi^- \rightarrow n + \pi^-$ suggested that $\Delta S = 2$ transitions might not take place. If such terms as $\bar{\psi}_n \gamma_\mu (1 + \gamma_5)\psi_{\Sigma^+}$ were added, where the strangeness and charge are opposite, transitions such as the Ξ-nucleon decay would be allowed. In the notation of the diagrams, $\Xi^- + \bar{\Sigma}^0 \rightarrow n + \overline{\Sigma^+} = \Xi^- \rightarrow n + \Sigma^0 + \overline{\Sigma^+} = n + \pi^-$.

Strange particles are then included in the Puppi triangle representation by adding another vertex to both the positive and negative triangles to form a tetrahedron.[4] This is shown in Figure 4-1 by dotted lines. Even as the restrictions on baryon pairs at the upper vertices are such that they must be able to annihilate virtually to produce a π^+ or π^- meson, the additional positive and negative vertices are restricted to baryon pairs which are equivalent to a K^+ or K^--meson, respectively. This *conjecture* leads to specific restrictions on strange particle decay; the transitions, $\Sigma^+ \rightarrow \mu^+(\text{or } e^+) + n + \nu$, $K^\pm \rightarrow \pi^\pm + \nu + \bar{\nu}$, $\overline{K}^0 \rightarrow \pi^- + \mu^+(\text{or } e^+) + \nu$, and $K^0 \rightarrow \pi^+ + \mu^-(\text{or } e^-) + \bar{\nu}$ are forbidden. These restrictions are summarized in a rule $\Delta S = +\Delta Q$, which is to say that in a weak interaction involving change in strangeness of baryons or mesons, the change in strangeness must be equal to the change in charge.

No events of the type $K^\pm \rightarrow \pi^\pm + \nu + \bar{\nu}$ have been observed, although this mode is easily observable experimentally and the decay probability is not inhibited by limited phase space. Likewise, no decay $\Sigma^+ \rightarrow \mu^+(\text{or } e^+) + n + \nu$ has been observed. This is at present less significant since all lepton decays of hyperons seem to be inhibited,[5] and the degree of forbiddenness implied by the limited information concerning the lack of Σ^+-decays is not yet striking.

Examination of the K^0 decays and K^0 interactions is interesting because of the relevance of experimental results to the $\Delta Q = \Delta S$ rule, and also to the importance of $\Delta S = 2$ transitions. The mass and the width, $\hbar/\tau$, where τ is the mean life of the particles $K_2{}^0$ and $K_1{}^0$ (Section 2.2), can be considered as the real and imaginary parts of the characteristic energies of these states. Even as the widths or half lives differ as different final states are available because of the different symmetries of the $K_2{}^0$ and $K_1{}^0$; the available virtual states will differ, the self energy resulting from the virtual transitions will differ, and the $K_1{}^0$ and $K_2{}^0$ masses will differ.[6]

Virtual transitions of the form $\langle K^0|I\rangle\langle I|K^0\rangle$, where I is an intermediate state which does not connect K^0 and $\overline{K}^0$, will be independent of the relative phase of the K^0 and $\overline{K}^0$ and will contribute equally to the mass of the $K_1{}^0 = 2^{-1/2}\,(|K^0\rangle + |\overline{K}^0\rangle)$, and the $K_2{}^0 = 2^{-1/2}\,(|K^0\rangle - |\overline{K}^0\rangle)$. However, the strangeness changing transitions, $\langle K^0|I'\rangle\langle I'|\overline{K}^0\rangle$, will contribute differently to the two different linear combinations as a result in the difference in signs and hence symmetries. Consider the magnitude of the energy shifts induced by the virtual transitions, $\overline{K}^0 \to p + \bar{p} \to K^0$, and the inverse. From second order perturbation theory, the energy shift will have the form:

$$\Delta E = \langle K^0|(p + \bar{p})\rangle\langle(p + \bar{p})|\overline{K}^0\rangle/(m_K - 2m_p)$$

Since the transitions $\overline{K}^0 \to p + \bar{p}$ and $p + \bar{p} \to K^0$ involve a change in strangeness, these must proceed by the weak interaction and the matrix elements will be approximately equal to the product of the weak interaction coupling constant, $g/(\sqrt{\hbar c}) \approx 10^{-7}$, and a characteristic energy. If this energy is taken to be the order of the K-meson mass, ΔE would be of the order of $(g^2/\hbar c)$ $m_K{}^2/m_p$, or about 10^{-6} ev.

Consider, however, a transition in which the strangeness changes by 2 for one matrix element and not at all for the second. For example, $\langle K^0|(\Lambda^0 + \bar{n})\rangle\langle(\Lambda^0 + \bar{n})|\overline{K}^0\rangle$. If a $\Delta S = 2$ transition is allowed for weak interactions, the matrix element $\langle K^0|(\overline{\Lambda^0} + n)\rangle$ should be of the magnitude of $[g/(\sqrt{\hbar c})]\,m_K$. However, the transition $\Lambda^0 + n \to \overline{K}_0$, involving no strangeness change, can proceed by the strong interactions and will have a magnitude $[G/(\sqrt{}\hbar c)]\, m_K$, where $G^2/\hbar c$ is the strong interaction coupling constant of the magnitude of 1. The energy shift in this case will be: $\Delta E \approx (gG/\hbar c)\, m_K{}^2/m_p \approx 10$ ev. A measurement of the energy difference will then indicate whether $\Delta S = 2$ transitions are allowed in such weak interactions.

As a definite example, consider an interaction which produces K^0-mesons, such as $\pi^- + p \rightarrow \Lambda^0 + K^0$. The K^0-meson wave function can be written as a function of time:

$$\psi = 2^{-1/2}[|K_1{}^0\rangle \exp(-i\omega_1 t - \lambda_1 t) + |K_2{}^0\rangle \exp(-i\omega_2 t - \lambda_2 t)]$$

where $\omega = mc^2/\hbar$ and $\lambda = 1/(2\tau)$, m and τ representing the mass and mean life, respectively. Noting that $|K_1{}^0\rangle = 2^{-1/2}(|K^0\rangle + |\overline{K}{}^0\rangle)$ and $|K_2{}^0\rangle = 2^{-1/2}(|K^0\rangle - |\overline{K}{}^0\rangle)$, we have for the intensity of $|\overline{K}{}^0\rangle$ as a function of time, for times $t \ll \tau_2$; $\langle \overline{K}{}^0|\psi\rangle^2 = 1 + \exp(-2\lambda_1 t) - 2\exp(-\lambda_1 t)\cos(\omega_1 - \omega_2)\,t$. The intensity of $|\overline{K}{}^0\rangle$ can be measured by observation of the existence of reactions such as $\overline{K}{}^0 + p \rightarrow \Sigma^+ + \pi$, which discriminate between K^0 and $\overline{K}{}^0$.

Careful measurements[7] on the reaction chain, $K^+ + X = K^0 + X'$, $\overline{K}{}^0 + X \rightarrow (\Sigma \text{ or } \Lambda) + \pi + X'$, where X represents nuclei in a propane bubble chamber, have determined the relative intensity of $\overline{K}{}^0$ as a function of time. Measurements of the distance between the K^0-producing interaction and the point of production of the hyperon, together with the momentum of the K-meson deduced from the kinematics of the reactions, allow a determination of the time elapsed. Figure 4-2 shows the intensity of $\overline{K}{}^0$ as a function of time for various values of $(\omega_1 - \omega_2) = (m_1 - m_2)\, c^2/\hbar$ measured in units of λ. Experimental results indicate a value of $(m_1 - m_2)\, c^2 = 1.5 \pm .2\hbar/\tau$, or about 10^{-5} ev. This excludes then, the possibility that $\Delta S = 2$ transitions are allowed by weak interactions as represented in this theory. The conclusion is not completely general as leptonic decays and mesonic decays of certain symmetries will not[8] contribute to the mass difference in any case.

In the same experiment, decays of the type $K \rightarrow e^+(e^-) + \pi^-(\pi^+) + \nu(\bar{\nu})$, were observed. If the $\Delta S = \Delta Q$ rule were valid, only the $\overline{K}{}^0$ will contribute to the e^- decays, and the probability of such decays should follow the same curve of Figure 4-2 as the hyperon production. Preliminary results are not in accord with this expectation.[9]

A basic postulate of the universal Fermi interaction view is that there is one coupling constant which holds for all weak interactions, those which preserve strangeness and those which change strangeness. Decays of strongly interacting particles, mesons and baryons, involve renormalization effects which relate to the virtual strong transitions which are available. To the extent which these are not important, or contribute in the same way to each kind of baryon, we should expect the lifetime for

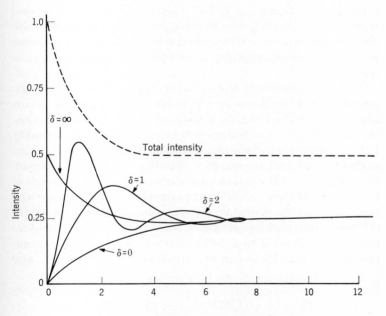

The time, t, is measured in units of the K_1^0 lifetime, τ_1.

Fig. 4-2. Plots of the intensity of $\overline{K^0}$ versus time in a beam which starts as pure K^0 at $t = 0$. δ represents the rest energy of the K_1^0 minus that of K_2^0 in multiples of $\hbar/\tau_1$. For all values of δ, the total intensity for $K^0 + \overline{K^0}$ is given by the dotted curve.

leptonic decays of all baryons to be proportional to the available phase space. Such a calculation[10] gives a branching ratio of 5.6 and 1.6% for the easily detectable hyperon to lepton decays, $\Sigma^- \rightarrow e^- + n + \bar{\nu}$, and $\Lambda^0 \rightarrow e^- + p + \bar{\nu}$, respectively. Experimental values[5] for these branching ratios are about an order of magnitude smaller. Muonic decays such as $\Sigma^- \rightarrow \mu^- + n + \bar{\nu}'$ and $\Lambda^0 \rightarrow \mu^- + p + \bar{\nu}'$, which were expected to occur with branching ratios of 2.5 and 0.3%, respectively, are experimentally somewhat difficult to separate from the pionic decays, but they also seem to occur with small probability. Although $\Sigma^+ \rightarrow e^+ + n$ (or Λ^0) $+ \nu$ decay, which violates the $\Delta S = \Delta Q$ rule, has not been observed, the experimental upper limit of about 0.1% for the branching ratio is not much smaller than that observed for other hyperon leptonic decays. In accordance with the charged current or tetrahedron scheme, no baryon or meson is known to decay emitting a neutrino pair, electron pair, or muon pair.

The most important lepton decay mode of the charged K-meson is the decay $K^+ \rightarrow \mu^+ + \nu'$ or $K^- \rightarrow \mu^- + \bar{\nu}'$, which occurs about 65% of the time. As a result of the $V - A$ interaction, the chirality of decay leptons will be $\pm v/c$, where the chirality is the polarization along the direction of propagation. By experiment, leptons have negative chirality and antileptons positive chirality. Such a polarization can be considered the result of interference of states of different parity; in this case, s-wave and $p_{1/2}$- wave states. A lepton state can be considered as an incoherent superposition of states with an angular momentum component of $+1/2$ in a z-direction and states with a z-component of $-1/2$. These can be written as $\psi^+ = aS^+ + bP^+$ and

$$\psi^- = aS^- + bP^-, \text{ where } S^+ = Y_0^0\uparrow, \ S^- = Y_0^0\downarrow$$

$$P^+ = -\sqrt{(1/3)}Y_1^0\uparrow + \sqrt{(2/3)}Y_1^1\downarrow; \ P^-$$

$$= \sqrt{(1/3)}Y_1^0\downarrow - \sqrt{(2/3)}Y_1^{-1}\uparrow$$

If we choose the direction of quantization to be the direction of emission, $\theta = 0$ (where the contribution of orbital angular momentum to the projected total is 0), we have $\psi^+ = (a - b)\uparrow$ and $\psi^- = (a + b)\downarrow$. The polarization of the state in this direction is

$$\frac{\langle\psi^+|\sigma_z|\psi^+\rangle + \langle\psi^-|\sigma_z|\psi^-\rangle}{\langle\psi^+|\psi^+\rangle + \langle\psi^-|\psi^-\rangle} = \frac{(-2\mathrm{Re}\ ab^*)}{(a^2 + b^2)} \equiv A \tag{2}$$

From the $V - A$ interaction we have, $A = -v/c$ for leptons and $A = v/c$ for antileptons.

Now consider the decays $K^+ \rightarrow \mu^+ + \nu'$ and $K^+ \rightarrow e^+ + \nu$. Taking the axis of quantization as the direction of emission and noting that the K-meson spin is 0, we have for the final wave function:

$$\psi = \psi_{(\nu)}{}^+\psi_{(\mu)}{}^- = (a_\nu - b_\nu)\uparrow_\nu(a_\mu + b_\mu)\downarrow_\mu$$

or $\tag{3}$

$$\psi = \psi_{(\nu)}{}^-\psi_{(\mu)}{}^+ = (a_\nu + b_\nu)\downarrow_\nu(a_\mu - b_\mu)\uparrow_\mu$$

For the neutrino $v/c = -1$, therefore, $a_\nu/b_\nu = 1$, and the neutrinos are emitted with negative chirality. Since the K-meson has spin 0, the antileptons, the positron and positive muon must be emitted with negative chirality, a transition which is forbidden to the degree of $1 - v/c \colon |\psi|^2 = (a_\mu{}^2 + 2a_\mu b_\mu + b_\mu{}^2) = (1 - v_\mu/c)$. For $K^+ \rightarrow e^+ + \nu$, $|\psi|^2 = (1 - v_e/c)$. To arrive at the absolute transition probabilities, these factors must be multiplied by the available phase space, dN/dE, and by a coupling constant. The phase space is simply calculated using $dN = 4\pi\ V\ p^2dp/h^3$, $E = \sqrt{(p_\mu{}^2 + m_\mu{}^2)} + p$. With straightforward arithmetic, we find the ratios of muon to electron emission to be

$$(m_\mu/m_e)^2[1 - (m_\mu/m_K)^2]^2/[1 - (m_e/m_K)^2]^2 \approx 4\cdot10^4$$

The electronic decay, which has not been observed, is expected to be very rare. Exactly the same arguments hold for the pion decays.[11] If the effective couplings were the same, the ratio of K-muon to pion-muon decay transition rates should be equal to $[1 - (m_\mu/m_K)^2]^2/[1 - (m_\mu/m_\pi)^2]^2 \approx 5$. Instead, the value is about 1.5; the leptonic decays of the strange mesons are weak, even as the leptonic decays of the strange baryons are weak.

4.2. Tau-Theta Problem

The neutral K-meson is known to decay into two pions, the theta mode, and into three pions, the tau mode. Dalitz[12] pointed out that it might be possible to determine the spin of the K-meson, and if parity is conserved in the decay, the parity, by examination of the momentum spectrum in the tau decay. The contradictions which became evident in these studies led Lee and Yang to their crucial examinations of parity nonconservation in weak interactions.

Consider the theta or two pion decay mode: since the pions have spin 0 and two pions have even intrinsic parity; the spin j of the K-meson must be the same as the orbital angular momentum, l, of the pions and the parity must be $(-1)^l$; therefore, the decay must be restricted to 0^+, 1^-, 2^+, $\cdots$ states, where the number represents the orbital angular momentum and the superscript the parity.

We can consider the tau mode decay of the K^+, $K^+ \rightarrow \pi^+ + \pi^- + \pi^+$, with the two positive pions making up a di-pion which decays into the two pions. Since these are identical bosons, the di-pion states must be restricted to the states 0^+, 2^+, $\cdots$. We can consider now the probability of finding a slow negative pion. In the absence of a very strong interaction, the pion final states will be approximately plane wave states and the probability that two particles are within a region of radius r is approximately $(r/\lambda)^l / \{1 \cdot 3 \cdots (2l - 1)\}^2$ for $\lambda \gg r$. The rate of emission or flux of slow π^- will then be approximately proportional to the probability of binding the π^- in the volume of radius r occupied by the K-meson multiplied by its velocity v, or $(r/\lambda)^l \cdot v$ which is proportional to $p^{(l+1)}$, where p is the π^- momentum. We see immediately that an s-wave negative pion which adds zero angular momentum and odd parity to the di-pion states, results in tau states 0^-, 2^-, etc., which are not among the possible theta states. We can carry through similar arguments concerning slow π^+-mesons. This di-pion, consisting of a π^- and π^+, will have the same possible states as the theta. An s-wave π^+ will then result in tau states 0^-, 1^+, 2^-, etc. Again, these are not among possible theta states. Our conclusion is: if the theta and tau are parity-conserving decay modes of the same particle, each pion in tau decay must have an angular momentum of at least 1 with respect to the center of mass of the other two pions, and the energy spectrum of slow pions must then be such that $dN/dE \approx p^2$, or a higher power of momentum. The experimental results indicate that the pion intensity varies as p, not p^2; there are too many slow pions from tau decay; either the theta and tau mode result from the decay of mesons of different parity, or parity is not conserved in the decay.

Early experimental analysis of the decay of tau-mesons concerned events found in nuclear emulsion plates exposed to cosmic radiation. Later, beams of K^+-mesons were produced at the bevatron, and definitive measurements were made of the decays of K^+-mesons in emulsions exposed to these beams.[13] The reasonably low energy of the pions facilitated these researches as two or three of the pions could be stopped and their ranges measured in moderate size emulsion blocks.

It seemed more and more probable that the tau and theta particles were identical as these experiments demonstrated with ever-increasing accuracy, the equivalence of their mass, lifetime,[14] and interaction behavior; that is, the same tau-theta ratio was observed under varying conditions.[15]

A more detailed analysis substantiates the qualitative theoretical arguments stated here, and together with the experimental data, suggests strongly that the K-meson spin is 0. We consider again the tau decay. Its Q-value is about 75 Mev and the maximum center of mass energy of a decay pion is about 50 Mev. This is sufficiently small that we make no great error in neglecting relativistic effects. Furthermore, the wavelength of the pion will be larger than the region of interaction, taken usually as the order of $1 \cdot 10^{-13}$ centimeter. We shall write the decay amplitude for a K-meson spin of J as a coherent sum of amplitudes $A_{L,l}$ representing the various possible combinations of L and l, which indicate the spin of the fictitous di-pion and the angular momentum of the π^-, respectively. It is convenient to choose the negative pion's direction as the direction of quantization so that the π^- will have no component of orbital angular momentum in this direction. The partial amplitudes will then have the form

$$A_{L,l} = a_{L,l}\Sigma_m\langle l,0,L,m|l,L,J,m\rangle Y_L{}^m(\theta,\phi)$$

where the Clebsch-Gordan coefficient connects the state of the K-meson with spin J and component m in the direction of quantization to the states of the di-pion and the π^-. The elements $A_{L,l}$ will be complex functions of p and q, the momentum of the negative pion in the center of mass and that of the decay pion in the center of mass of the di-pion, respectively. The effects of the centrifugal barrier which we have considered suggest that the square of these elements will have a form approximately proportional to $(pr/\hbar)^l\cdot(qr/\hbar)^L/[(1\cdot3\cdots(2l-1))\cdot(1\cdot3\cdots(2L-1))]^2\,\mathrm{d}N/\mathrm{d}E$, where $\mathrm{d}N/\mathrm{d}E$ is the number of states in phase space per unit energy.

In general, the constraints imposed by the conservation of energy and momentum are such that the transition probability ω for a three-particle decay can be expressed as a function of two variables. It is convenient to choose these as the total energy, W, of two of the particles; then [16]:

$$\omega(W_1, W_2) = 2\pi\hbar^{-1}\left|M(W_1, W_2)\right|^2\,\mathrm{d}N/\mathrm{d}E \qquad (4)$$

where $\mathrm{d}N/\mathrm{d}E$ is the density of states factor and $M(W_1, W_2)$ is the matrix element. The phase space factor $\mathrm{d}N/\mathrm{d}E = \rho\,(W_1, W_2)$ can be written as:

$$\rho(W_1, W_2) = \Omega^2 h^{-6} \int \mathrm{d}^3p_1 \int \mathrm{d}^3p_2 \int \mathrm{d}^3p_3 \left(\sum_i p\right)$$
$$\delta\left(M_{\mathrm{K}} - \sum_i w_i\right) \delta(w_i - W_1)\, \delta(w_2 - W_2) \qquad (5)$$

where the δ-functions impose the constraints corresponding to conservation of momentum and energy, and the constraints representing the evaluation at specific energies, W_1 and W_2: the w_i represent the total energies as variables of integration.

The integral over p_1 in (5) can be expressed as usual as $\int 4\pi p_1{}^2 \, dp_1$. For any value of p_1, the constraint imposed by the conservation of momentum requires the loci of the values of p_2 to lie on a surface of revolution (Fig. 4-3a), and the integration

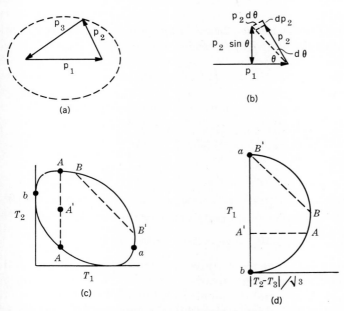

(a)

(b)

(c)

(d)

Fig. 4-3. (a) Conservation of momentum and energy in tau decay requires that for fixed momentum vector p_1, the tip of vector p_2 be constrained to lie on a surface of revolution about p_1. (b) Shows the relationship between the differentials in θ and p_2. (c) Dalitz-Fabri plot for tau decay at rest. The kinetic energy T_1 of the negative pion is plotted against that of one of the positive pions. If determined only by available phase space, the density of decay events on such a plot would be uniform. (d) Symmetric form of the Dalitz-Fabri plot for positive tau decay. T_1 is the kinetic energy of the negative pion; T_2 and T_3 that of the two positive pions. Phase space density is also uniform for this plot.

over p_2 and p_3 will be equivalent to evaluating the volume of the figure, as shown in Figure 4-3b, which is equal to:

$$\iint p_2 \, d\theta \, dp_2 2\pi p_2 \sin \theta = \int 2\pi p_2{}^2 \, dp_2 \int d \, (\cos \theta) \qquad (6)$$

The square of the total energy of particle 3 is given by $w_3{}^2 = p_3{}^2 + m_3{}^2 = p_1{}^2 + p_2{}^2 + 2p_1 p_2 \cos \theta + m_3{}^2$, in units such that $c = 1$.

At fixed w_1 and w_2, $2w_3 dw = 2p_1 p_2 d(\cos \theta)$. Using this relation and the identity $p_i dp_i = w_i dw_i$, we have:

$$\rho(W_1, W_2) = 8\pi^2 \Omega^2 h^{-6} \iiint w_1 w_2 w_3 \, dw_1 \, dw_2 \, dw_3 \qquad (7)$$

$$\delta(w_1 - W_1) \, \delta(w_2 - W_2) \, \delta(w_3 - W_3)$$

where the last δ-function is equivalent to, and replaces, the conservation of energy constraint of (5). Performing the intergration:

$$\rho(W_1, W_2) = 8\pi^2 \Omega^2 h^{-6} \, W_1 W_2 W_3 \qquad (8)$$

The quantity $R(W_1, W_2) = M(W_1, W_2) (2W_1)^{1/2} (2W_2)^{1/2} (2W_3)^{1/2}$ is a Lorentz invariant matrix element; using this we have:

$$\omega(W_1, W_2) = 2\pi \hbar^{-1} \pi^2 \Omega^2 h^{-6} \left| R(W_1, W_2) \right|^2 \qquad (9)$$

Since $W_i = m_i + T_i$, where T_i is the kinetic energy and m_i (the rest mass) is an invariant, the variable W_i can be replaced by T_i in (9), and the number of states per unit energy is a constant for equal intervals of kinetic energy of any two particles. In the classical limit, $T_i \ll m_i |R|^2 = 8m_1 m_2 m_3 |M|^2$ and the relation

$$\omega(T_1, T_2) = 2\pi \hbar^{-1} \pi^2 \Omega^2 h^{-6} 8m_1 m_2 m_3 \left| M(T_1, T_2) \right|^2 \qquad (10)$$

holds. It is this relation which we shall use for the discussion of the tau decay.

From the consideration of Figure 4-3a, it is clear that for any value of one momentum, p, the extreme values of p_2 and p_3 will be such that the momenta are colinear and $p_1 + p_2 + p_3 = 0$.

From this condition on the momentum, and the conservation of energy, we have then: $T_2 + T_3 + \sqrt{(T_2 T_3)} = Q/2$, which represents the boundary of the kinematically allowed region in a space of coordinates T_1 and T_2. This is usually called a Dalitz or Dalitz-Fabri plot. For tau decays, each experimentally measured event can be shown as a point on such a plot (Fig. 4-3c). It is easy to show that the semimajor axis of the ellipse is $Q/\sqrt{6}$, the semiminor axis is $Q/\sqrt{18}$, and hence the area is $\pi Q^2/(6 \cdot \sqrt{3})$. Since this is the integral over dT_1 and dT_2, we can immediately write the phase space density for the tau decay as $dN/dE = V^2 h^{-6} \pi^3 m_\pi{}^3 Q^2 \cdot 4/(3\sqrt{3})$.

The separate consideration of the two π^+ mesons is, of course, a fiction, experimentally as well as theoretically. It is convenient to present the data for tau decay in a symmetric form; in a plot in which the variables are $|T_2 - T_3|/\sqrt{3}$ and T_1. With these variables, the Dalitz-Fabri diagram is now a semicircle as shown in Figure 4-3d. Again, from geometric considerations (the area is still $\pi Q^2/(6 \cdot \sqrt{3})$), we see the phase space density for production of a π^- meson of energy T is $dN/dE = 32\pi^2 V^2 h^{-6} (m_\pi/\sqrt{3})^3$ $Q^2 (1 - \epsilon)^{1/2} \epsilon^{1/2} T_{\max}{}^{-1} dT$ where $T_{\max}$ is $2Q/3$ and $\epsilon = T/T_{\max}$.

It is evident that if the decay interaction is dominated by phase space considerations, experimental events plotted on the Dalitz-Fabri plot should evenly populate it. This distribution will be distorted if the matrix elements exhibit momentum or angle dependences. Table 4-1 shows the form of the amplitudes for various values of spins and parities assuming that only the lowest values of angular momentum, l and L, are important for each value of J, and that only the centrifugal barrier effects are important sources of momentum dependence. Since it is evident that parity is not conserved, the distribution will be the square of the sums of the amplitudes for the different parities multiplied by unknown complex constants. If the π-π interactions are not extremely strong and the decay is invariant under time reversal, these coefficients will be nearly real.

The results of the experimental work[13] show that the distribution is approximately constant over the Dalitz-Fabri plot,

Table 4-1

Distribution of Pions in Tau Decay for Various Assignments of Spin and
Parity to the K-meson

$J\pi$	l	L	Momentum dependence	Angular dependence
$0-$	0	0	1	1
$0+$	—	—	—	—
$1-$	2	2	$p^2 q^2$	$\sin^2 \theta \cos^2 \theta$
$1+$	1	0	p	1
$2-$	2	0	p^2	1
$2-$	0	2	q^2	1
$2+$	1	2	pq^2	$\sin^2 \theta$

though there are somewhat fewer slow π^--mesons than one
would expect from pure phase space considerations. If the matrix
element is proportional to p, there will be few events near point b
on Figure 4-3d; if it is proportional to q_1, there will be few events
near point a. Angular dependence is observable in more complex
ways. For a given value of T, the point A' represents cos
$\theta = 0$ and A, cos $\theta = 1$. Equal intervals along the line represent
equal intervals of cos θ. From these considerations and from
inspection of Table 4-1, we see that spin 1 is ruled out. It is,
however, possible to find combinations of spin 2 (and spin 4)
amplitudes which are not in contradiction with the experimental
results. It is in order to add here that the observation of the
decay of the neutral K to two π^0-mesons excludes spin 1 for the
K^0-meson.

Final state interactions can influence the distribution; the
fact that there are fewer slow π^- mesons than expected on a
statistical picture may result from π-π interactions. The effect of
such interactions would be most striking if sharp scattering
resonances existed in the energy region involved in tau decay.
In case of a π^+-π^+ resonance, one would expect an increased
density of points along a line such as A'-A, while a π^--π^+ resonance would increase the density along a line at 45^0 such as B'-B.
There is no indication of such a resonance.

4.3. Hyperon Decays

It was pointed out in Section 2.2 that observations concerning the decay of polarized Λ^0 hyperons led to the first entirely firm conclusion that parity was not conserved in the nonleptonic decays of strange particles; i.e., decays which did not involve neutrinos. A detailed analysis of the Λ^0 decay is then informative.[17] The considerations hold generally for all hyperon decays.

We consider a polarized Λ^0 with spin 1/2 and a component of spin in a z-direction of 1/2. We assume that the Λ^0 will not conserve parity in decay and will then decay into $S_{1/2}$ and $P_{1/2}$ states of the nucleon and pion with respective complex amplitudes A and B, such that A and B have a phase difference of η. We use a convenient normalization, $A^2 + B^2 = 1$. The wave function in the rest frame of the Λ^0 will then be:

$$\psi = A\psi_s + B\psi_p, \text{ where } \psi_s = CY_0{}^0\uparrow = [1/(\sqrt{4\pi})]\uparrow$$

and

$$\psi_p = C'Y_1{}^1\downarrow + C''Y_1{}^0\uparrow = -(1/\sqrt{4\pi})\,(\cos\theta\uparrow + \sin\theta\downarrow e^{i\phi})$$

Here the C's are the appropriate Clebsch-Gordan coefficients, and $\uparrow$ and $\downarrow$ are the proton spin wave functions for $m_z = 1$, and $m_z = -1$, respectively. The angles θ and ϕ are the decay angles. It is conventional to define θ as the direction of proton emission with respect to z. The intensity will then be:

$$dN/d\Omega = \langle\psi|\psi\rangle = (1/4\pi)\,(1 - \alpha\cos\theta), \text{ where } \alpha = 2|A|\cdot|B|\cdot\cos\eta$$

If the interaction is invariant under time reversal, the relative phases of the matrix elements to different parity states, A and B will be 0 or $180°$ modified by the final state $\pi^- + \mathrm{p}$ scattering according to Watson's theorem (Section 5.7). The S and $P_{1/2}$ scattering phase shifts are small at the relevant energy 37 Mev, the Q value of the Λ^0, so if time reversal invariance holds, $\cos\eta$ will be very nearly 1 or -1. If the interaction were invariant under charge conjugation, the relative phase of transitions to states of opposite parity would be $\pi/2$. Again, there would be a negligible effect resulting from the final state phase shifts so cos η would be nearly 0.

Experimentally, one measures, always, the product $P\alpha$, where P is the polarization which, for spin 1/2 particles, can be defined simply as $[I(\uparrow) - I(\downarrow)]/[I(\uparrow) + I(\downarrow)]$ where $I(\uparrow)$ represents the intensity with spin up. The proton intensity will be $dN/d\Omega = 1 - P\alpha \cos \theta$. Measurements of asymmetries[18] in the reaction $\pi^- + p \rightarrow \Lambda^0 + K^0$ have resulted in values of $P\alpha$ as high as 0.7. Since $P \leq 1$, then, the absolute value of α must be ≥ 0.7, the absolute value of cos η must be ≥ 0.7, and the decay interaction must violate charge conjugation invariance.

This large value of $P\alpha$, reflecting the observation of a large up-down asymmetry with respect to the plane of production, or a large value of the average component of proton decay momentum with respect to the Λ spin direction, has been used to determine the spin of the lambda. If the spin of the lambda is 1/2, the absolute value of $(\cos \theta)_{\mathrm{av}}$, where $\cos \theta = p_z/|p|$, will equal $1/3|\alpha P|$ where p is the proton momentum, z represents the direction of the lambda spin and the average is taken over all decays. The maximum value of this average direction cosine will then be 1/3 for $|\alpha| = 1$. If the spin is large, the maximum allowed value is much reduced, a result which can be understood qualitatively in the classical limit. Consider a lambda of spin $l \gg 0$, aligned such that the spin axis coincides with a polarization direction z, such as defined by the perpendicular to the production plane in the reaction $\pi^- + p \rightarrow \Lambda^0 + K^0$. Since the decay proton and pion can carry off angular momentum only in a direction perpendicular to their line of flight, the decays would be restricted to the plane perpendicular to the spin axis and $(\cos \theta)_{\mathrm{av}}$ will be equal to 0. Although the uncertainty principle relaxes this condition to allow decay angles which deviate from this plane up to l^{-1} radians, even with the maximum decay asymmetry the absolute value of $(\cos \theta)_{\mathrm{av}}$ will still be small for these completely polarized lambdas. Decays which occur such that $(\cos \theta)$ is large, must then result from states which are not so strongly polarized—states in which the spin axis lies at a large angle with respect to the z-direction. Since the decays are asymmetric with respect to the spin direction alone (it is the only internal direction defined for the lambda), such decays will contribute little to any asymmetry in the z-direction, and none in any other direction if parity is conserved in the production process (Section 2.4). These qualitative conclusions, made more precise and sharpened by the construction of test functions which heavily weigh events in which $(\cos\theta)$ is large,[31] together with the experimental results,[32] exclude the possibility that the lambda spin is greater than $1/2$. In general, this method results in an upper limit to the spin and is most useful when the spin is small, the asymmetry coefficient is large, and a strongly polarized sample of hyperons is available.

Unless the sign of the Λ^0 polarization and its magnitude can be derived from a detailed consideration of the production amplitudes, which is at best difficult, and has not been done, one cannot determine the sign of α from observations of decay asymmetries, and one needs to find fortuitously a large value of P to put only a lower limit on the value of α. This sign and value can be determined, however, by measuring the polarization of the protons emitted from unpolarized Λ^0's.[19]

We take the direction of emission of the proton as the direction of quantization. The unpolarized Λ^0-wave function can be written: $\psi = (1/\sqrt{2})\,(\epsilon_+\psi_+ + \epsilon_-\psi_-)$ where the ϵ are orthonormal vectors, i.e., $\epsilon_i\epsilon_j = \delta_{ij}$, introduced as a formal way of representing the incoherence of the "spin up" and "spin down" Λ^0's, ψ_+ and ψ_-, respectively. The decay wave functions can be written as usual; for spin up Λ^0: $\psi_+ = A\uparrow - B\,(\cos\theta\uparrow + \sin\theta\downarrow\,e^{i\phi})$, for spin down Λ^0: $\psi_- = A\downarrow - B\,(-\cos\theta\downarrow + \sin\theta\uparrow\,e^{-i\phi})$. Since θ, the angle of emission of the proton equals $0°$, $\psi_+ = A\uparrow - B\uparrow$ while $\psi_- = (A\downarrow + B\downarrow)$. The proton polarization, P, in the z-direction will be the expectation value for the spin in the z-direction $\langle\psi|\sigma_z|\psi\rangle$ divided by the total intensity $\langle\psi|\psi\rangle$. Noting that $\sigma_z|\uparrow\rangle = |\uparrow\rangle$ and $\sigma_z|\downarrow\rangle = -|\downarrow\rangle$, we have $P = -2|A|\cdot|B|\cos\eta = -\alpha$. For α positive, the proton is polarized opposite to its direction of flight in the center of mass system of the Λ^0 to a degree α.

The measurement of longitudinal polarization is difficult

because parity conserving interactions cannot produce, or discriminate between, longitudinally polarized particles. However, protons emitted perpendicular to the line of flight in the rest system of a Λ^0 in motion will have a component of polarization perpendicular to their own direction of motion in the laboratory. Such protons are scattered preferentially to the left or right with respect to a plane defined by the momentum vector and polarization vector of the lambda. Such asymmetric scattering has been carefully studied, as a function of element, scattering angle, and proton energy, in the course of investigations of polarized protons and optical models of nuclei. Analyses of results of experiments in which the polarization of protons from Λ^0 decay was measured by observing the proton scattering from carbon in a propane bubble chamber [20] and in carbon plates of spark chambers[21] show that α is negative; that is, the proton is polarized along its direction of emission. These measurements can then tell us the value of $|A| \cdot |B| \cdot \cos \eta$, but not the values of A or B, or whether $A < B$ or $B < A$.

An important question is then left to us, undetermined by the previous considerations. Which is larger, A, the s-wave transition amplitude, or B, the p-wave transition amplitude? This can be determined by measuring the polarization of protons emitted from polarized lambdas. Consider, for definiteness, decays of polarized lambdas such that the lambdas are polarized in the z-direction and the decay is in the xz-plane. Using the wave functions for polarized protons written previously, we find for the z polarization:

$$\frac{\langle \psi | \sigma_z | \psi \rangle}{\langle \psi | \psi \rangle} = \frac{A^2 - 2AB \cos \eta \cos \theta + B^2 \cos (2\theta)}{(1 - \alpha \cos \theta)} \tag{11}$$

where θ is the angle of decay.

Recalling that $\sigma_x | \uparrow \rangle = | \downarrow \rangle$ and $\sigma_x | \downarrow \rangle = | \uparrow \rangle$, we have for the x polarization:

$$\frac{\langle \psi | \sigma_x | \psi \rangle}{\langle \psi | \psi \rangle} = \frac{-2AB \cos \eta \sin \theta + B^2 \sin (2\theta)}{(1 - \alpha \cos \theta)} \tag{12}$$

and the y polarization is 0. The x polarization, or in-out polarization, particularly at $\theta = \pi/4$, is dependent upon the intensity of the $p_{1/2}$ state, so the values of A and B can be determined. Measurements of this polarization show that the s-wave decay intensity is about five times as large as the p-wave intensity.[21,22]

While the discussion of this section has referred to lambda decays, the remarks are also relevant to sigma and Ξ decays.

4.4. The $\Delta I = 1/2$ Rule

Consideration of the relative probabilities of the mesonic decays of the K-meson suggests important conclusions concerning weak interactions. In the absence of selection rules or strong interactions between the emitted particles, one might expect that the probability of decay via a certain mode would be proportional to the phase space available. We have shown (Section 4.2) that the phase space for the 3π decay of the charged K-meson is $(dN/dE)_{3\pi} = 4\pi^3 \ V^2 h^{-6} \ (m_\pi/\sqrt{3})^3 \ Q_{3\pi}^2$. We must compare this with the phase space for the 2π-mode; here $dN/dp = Vh^{-3} \ 4\pi p^2$. Since the $Q_{2\pi}$-value is 219 Mev, it will be a reasonably adequate approximation to treat the pions relativistically; then $E = pc$ and p will be about equal to $m_\pi c$. Then $(dN/dE)_{2\pi} = Vh^{-3} \ 4\pi m_\pi^2 c$ and the ratio $(dN/dE)_{2\pi}/(dN/dE)_{3\pi} = 3(\sqrt{3})\pi^{-2}h^3 V^{-1}Q_{3\pi}^{-2}m_\pi^{-1}c$. For an interaction volume $4/3 \ \pi$ $(\hbar/m_\pi c)^3$ this ratio is about 60:1, if the K-meson Compton wavelength is used for the radius of the interaction volume, the ratio is about 1800:1. Since the experimental ratio is about 3:1, it would seem that either the 3π decay is enhanced, perhaps by a strong π-π interaction, or the 2π decay is inhibited, perhaps by a selection rule.

A comparison of the K_1^0- and K^+- decays should be pertinent: the partial lifetime for $K^+ \rightarrow \pi^+ + \pi^0$ is about $5 \cdot 10^{-8}$ seconds, while the $K^0 \rightarrow 2\pi$ decay lifetime is about 10^{-10} seconds, a ratio of 500; comparable to the $2\pi/3\pi$ inhibiting factor just noted. All this suggests that the K^0 to 2π and the K^+ to 3π decays are normal, while the K^+ to $\pi^+ + \pi^0$ decay is forbidden.

Such results can be understood if the weak nonleptonic decays of strange particles obey a selection rule[23] such that $|\Delta I| = 1/2$. Since the third component of isotopic spin for the system $\pi^+ + \pi^0$ is $+1$, this state can have only isotopic spin 1 or 2, but not 0. Odd states of isotopic spin are antisymmetric upon the exchange of isotopic spin coordinates while even states are symmetric. Since for two identical bosons the over-all symmetry must be even, odd isotopic spin states must be antisymmetric in space and have odd angular momentum: 1, 3, $\cdots$; and even isotopic spin states will have even spin. Since the K-meson has 0 spin, the isotopic spin of the $\pi^+ - \pi^0$ state into which it decays must must be 2. Since the isotopic spin of the K-meson is 1/2, the decay to this state will be forbidden if only $|\Delta I| = 1/2$ transitions are allowed. The decays which do occur presumably are the result of charge dependent electromagnetic forces.

Since T_3 is equal to 0 for the K^0 decays, the $T = 0$ state with 0 angular momentum is a possible final state, and, if the $|\Delta I| = 1/2$ rule is valid, the only possible final state. The branching ratio $(\pi^+ + \pi^-)/(\pi^0 + \pi^0)$ from a pure $T = 0$ state is the ratio of the squares of the appropriate Clebsch-Gordan coefficients: $\langle 1\ 1\ 1\ -1|1\ 1\ 0\ 0\rangle^2/\langle 1\ 0\ 1\ 0|1\ 1\ 0\ 0\rangle^2 = 2$; that is, two thirds of the K_1^0 decays should be to the charged modes. Experimentally, the ratio is $.66\pm.04$, in good agreement with this analysis.[24]

We note that the selection rule is only approximate, inasmuch as the decay $K^+ \rightarrow \pi^+ + \pi^0$ does occur, though reduced in intensity by a factor of about 500. Since electromagnetic forces exist, isotopic spin cannot be a completely good quantum number. Indeed, one might expect impurities in the amplitude of the order of Δ/M, where Δ is the energy splitting of the members of isotopic spin multiplets and M is the mean particle mass. For pions and K-mesons this is of the order of a few percent— consistent with the $|\Delta I| = 3/2$ impurity of about 5% required to explain the $K^+ \rightarrow \pi^+ + \pi^0$ decay. An impurity of this magnitude would result in a deviation of about $\pm.04$ from the pure $|\Delta I| = 1/2$ result of $.667$ for the charged to total ratio of K_1^0-decays.

While it may be conceivable that such a restriction on weak interaction decays hold only for mesons, it would seem likely that decays of the Λ^0, with isotopic spin 0, should be to a state of isotopic spin 1/2. Conservation of charge and baryon number restricts the third component to the value of $-1/2$, completely determining the decay wave function in isotopic spin space to be $\sqrt{(2/3)}\ p\pi^- + \sqrt{(1/3)}\ n\pi^0$. The intensity of the charged decay will be twice that of the neutral decay, in agreement with the measured value[24] for the charged decay to neutral decay ratio of $1.9\pm.1$. Since the space wave functions are the same, according to this calculation, the asymmetries of the charged and neutral decay modes should be the same.

Effects of the restrictions imposed by the $|\Delta I| = 1/2$ rule on sigma decay are less definite since the sigma has isotopic spin 1, which allows its decay into either isotopic spin state 1/2 or 3/2. However, there exists a greater variety of experimental information for the sigmas. We can consider separately the decays of Σ^+ and Σ^- and investigate the relationships between these decays. Since the sigma has spin 1/2, decay, not nominally restricted by parity conservation, will take place to the $(s_{1/2}, I = 1/2)$ state, $(p_{1/2}, I = 1/2)$ state, $(s_{1/2}, I = 3/2)$ state, and the $(p_{1/2}, I = 3/2)$ state. We write the amplitudes for these states as U_1, U_{11}, U_3, U_{31}. Assuming invariance under time reversal, the phases of these amplitudes are, from Watson's theorem concerning the phases of final states, just the π-p scattering phase shifts for the respective states at the center of mass energy corresponding to the Q-value for the sigma decay. From analysis of π-p scattering, these are known to be small; therefore, we can treat the amplitudes as if they are real. We can then write the space and spin part of the isotopic spin 1/2 amplitude $A_1 = U_1 + U_{11}$, and the isotopic spin 3/2 amplitude $A_3 = U_3 + U_{31}$, where the quantities A_i can be considered two component vectors in an s-wave, p-wave plane, and the subscript i represents twice the isotopic spin.

A general statement of the $|\Delta I| = 1/2$ rule is such as to establish that the symmetry in isotopic spin space of the final state plus an isotopic spin 1/2 state is the same as that of the initial state. Formally the decay can then be considered as a transition from the initial state to a final state by the emission of a massless particle of isotopic spin 1/2 carrying neither momentum nor energy, usually called the spurion.[26] The relationship between strangeness and the third component of the spurion is $\Delta S/2 = I_3$, where ΔS is the change in strangeness.

Noting this, we can express the Σ^+ decay as $\Sigma^+ \rightarrow -\sqrt{(1/4)}\ T_{3/2}{}^{1/2}\ A_3 + T_{1/2}{}^{1/2}\ A_1$ and the Σ^- decay to $-\sqrt{(3/4)}\ T_{3/2}{}^{-3/2}\ A_3$, where the constants are the appropriate Clebsch-Gordan coefficients and the T's represent the isotopic spin wave functions of the pion-nucleon system. Expanding these total isotopic spin wave functions in π-nucleon states, we have $A^- = -\sqrt{(3/4)}A_3$, $A^0 = -\sqrt{(1/3)}A_1 - \sqrt{(1/6)}A_3$, and $A^+ = \sqrt{(2/3)}A_1 - \sqrt{(1/12)}A_3$, where A^+, A^0, and A^- represent the amplitudes for $\Sigma^+ \rightarrow n + \pi^+$, $\Sigma^+ \rightarrow p + \pi^0$, and $\Sigma^- \rightarrow n + \pi^-$, respectively. We note that then the $|\Delta I| = 1/2$ rule imposes the relationship $(\sqrt{2})A^0 + A^+ = A^-$.[27]

The squares of the amplitudes A^i are proportional to the decay rates to the modes i, or to the lifetimes of the states divided by the branching ratio. Experimental results then establish the equality of the absolute values of A^+, A^0, and A^- to better than 5 percent, a result which is in accord with the relationship required by the $|\Delta I| = 1/2$ rule. Since the length of the vectors are equal, the amplitudes must form a 45° right triangle in the s-wave and p-wave space as shown in Figure 4-4. Only the angle β is undetermined.

From the section on Λ^0-decay, we see that the decay distribution of the nucleons from polarized hyperons will have the form $dN/d(\cos \theta) = 1 - \alpha \cos \theta$, where θ is the angle between the directions of polarization and proton emission and $\alpha = 2A_s A_p \cos \eta/(A_s{}^2 + A_p{}^2)$ where A_s and A_p are the absolute values of the s-wave and p-wave decay amplitudes and η is the phase difference, here equal to 0. Then, from the geometry of Figure 4-4, we see that $\alpha^- = \sin \beta \cos \beta$, $\alpha^0 = \sin (\beta\text{-}45°) \cos (\beta\text{-}45°)$,

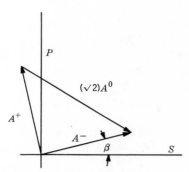

Fig. 4-4. The amplitudes A^+, A^-, and A^0 for the decay of Σ^+, Σ^-, and Σ^0 are represented by vectors in the s-wave, p-wave plane. The $\mid \Delta I \mid = 1/2$ rule requires that $(\sqrt{2})A^0 + A^+ = A^-$. The angle β remains undetermined.

and $\alpha^+ = \sin (\beta + 90°) \cos (\beta + 90°)$. All three asymmetries cannot be small, nor can all be very large.

Measurements concerning these asymmetries have been made by observing the pions from the decay of sigmas produced in the reactions $\pi^+ + p \rightarrow \Sigma^+ + K^{+28}$ and $\pi^- + n \rightarrow \Sigma^- + K^{+29}$ at 1.0 Gev. These observations establish that $\alpha^+ < 0.04 \pm 0.11$, $\alpha^0 > 0.75 \pm 0.17$, and $\alpha^- < 0.01 \pm 0.17$. These results are consistent with the $\mid \Delta I \mid = 1/2$ rule. Assuming that the rule is exact, the angle β in Figure 4-4 is determined to be $3 \pm 6°$.

The $\Delta I = 1/2$ rule might also hold for the leptonic decays. The change in baryon or meson isotopic spin would be represented by the emission of a spurion. Such a rule would include the $\Delta S = \Delta Q$ rule as a $\Delta S = -\Delta Q$ transition must change the third component of isotopic spin by $3/2$. Again preliminary results[9] are not in good agreement with this conjecture.

The $\mid \Delta I \mid = 1/2$ rule for mesonic decays does not follow simply from the current-current interaction. It is an additional constraint. The modifications, or amplifications to the intermediate boson theory required to include the $\mid \Delta I \mid = 1/2$ rule have been established.[30]

REFERENCES

1. R. Feynman and M. Gell-Mann, *Phys. Rev.*, 109, 193 (1958).
2. R. Marshak and E. C. G. Sudarshan, *Phys. Rev.*, 109, 1860 (1958); J. Sakurai, *Nuovo Cimento*, 7, 649 (1958).
3. G. Puppi, *Nuovo Cimento*, Ser. 9, 5, 505 (1948).
4. N. Dallaporta, *Nuovo Cimento*, 1, 962 (1953); M. Gell-Mann and A. H. Rosenfeld, *Ann. Rev. Nucl. Sci.*, 7, 407 (1957).
5. W. E. Humphrey, J. Kirz, A. H. Rosenfeld, J. Leitner, and Y. I. Rhee, *Phys. Rev. Letters*, 6, 478 (1961); B. Aubert, V. Brisson, J. Hennessy, P. Mittner, and J. Six, *Proc. of Aix-en-Provence Intern. Conf. on Elementary Particles*, C. E. N. Saclay (1961).
6. L. Okun and B. Pontecorvo, *Soviet Phys. JETP (English Transl.)*, 32, 1587 (1957) and *Soviet Phys. JETP (English Transl.)*, 5, 1297 (1957).
7. R. W. Birge, R. P. Ely, W. M. Powell, H. Huzita, W. F. Fry, J. A. Gaidos, S. V. Natali, R. B. Willman, and U. Camerini, *Proc. of the Tenth Ann. Intern. Conf. on High Energy Physics, 1960*, Interscience, New York, 1960; also Reference 25, Chapter 2.
8. S. L. Glashow, *Phys. Rev. Letters*, 6, 196 (1961).
9. R. P. Ely, W. M. Powell, H. White, M. Baldo-Ceolin, E. Calimani, S. Ciampollilo, O. Fabbri, F. Farini, C. Filippi, H. Huzita, G. Miari, U. Camerini, W. F. Fry, and S. Natali, *Phys. Rev. Letters*, 8, 132 (1962).
10. B. T. Feld, *Phys. Rev.*, 107, 797 (1957).
11. M. A. Ruderman and R. J. Finkelstein, *Phys. Rev.* 76, 1458 (1949).
12. R. H. Dalitz, *Phil. Mag.*, 44, 1068 (1953) and *Phys. Rev.*, 94, 1046 (1954).
13. J. Orear, G. Harris, and S. Taylor, *Phys. Rev.*, 102, 1676 (1956).
14. V. L. Fitch and R. M. Motley, *Phys. Rev.*, 105, 265 (1957); L. W. Alvarez, F. S. Crawford, M. Good, and M. L. Stevenson, *Phys. Rev.*, 101, 503 (1956).
15. M. Wigdoff, A. M. Shapiro, R. Schluter, D. M. Ritson, A. Pevsner, and V. P. Henri, *Phys. Rev.*, 104, 811 (1956); for equality of masses for τ and θ, see R. W. Birge, J. R. Peterson, D. H. Stork, and M. N. Whitehead, *Phys. Rev.*, 100, 430 (1955).
16. E. Fabri, *Nuovo Cimento*, 11, 479 (1954); M. Gell-Mann and A. H. Rosenfeld, *Ann. Rev. Nucl. Sci.*, 7, 407 (1957).
17. T. D. Lee, J. Steinberger, G. Feinberg, P. M. Kabir, and C. N. Yang, *Phys. Rev.* 106, 1367 (1957).
18. See Reference 14, Chapter 2.
19. T. D. Lee and C. N. Yang, *Phys. Rev.*, 108, 1353 (1957).
20. R. W. Birge and W. B. Fowler, *Phys. Rev. Letters*, 5, 254 (1960); J. Leitner, L. Gray, E. Harth, S. Lichtman, J. Westgard, M. Block, B. Brucker, A. Engler, R. Gessaroli, A. Kovacs, T. Kikuchi, C. Meltzer,

H. O. Cohn, W. Bugg, A. Pevsner, P. Schlein, M. Meer, N. T. Grinellini, L. Lendinara, L. Monari, and G. Puppi, *Phys. Rev. Letters*, **7**, 264 (1961). The latter refers to work in a helium bubble chamber.

21. E. F. Beall, B. Cork, D. Keefe, P. G. Murphy, and W. A. Wenzel, *Phys. Rev. Letters*, **7**, 285 (1961).

22. J. W. Cronin and O. E. Overseth, unpublished preprint, Princeton University, Princeton, New Jersey (1962).

23. M. Gell-Mann and A. Pais, *Proceedings of the Intern. Conf. on High Energy Physics*, Pergammon Press, London, 1955.

24. F. S. Crawford, M. Cresti, R. L. Douglass, M. L. Good, G. R. Kalbfleisch, M. L. Stevenson, and H. K. Ticho, *Phys. Rev. Letters*, **2**, 266 (1959).

26. G. Wentzel, *Phys. Rev.*, **101**, 1215 (1956).

27. M. Gell-Mann and A. H. Rosenfeld, *ibid.*

28. B. Cork, L. Kerth, W. A. Wenzel, J. W. Cronin, and R. L. Cool, *Phys. Rev.*, **120**, 1000 (1960); see also Reference 22.

29. P. Franzini, A. Garfinkel, J. Keren, A. Michelini, R. Plano, A. Prodell, M. Schwartz, J. Steinberger, and S. E. Wolf, *Bull. Amer. Phys. Soc.*, **5**, 224 (1960).

30. T. D. Lee and C. N. Yang, *Phys. Rev.*, **119**, 1410 (1960).

31. T. D. Lee and C. N. Yang, *Phys. Rev.*, **109**, 1755 (1958).

32. F. S. Crawford, M. Cresti, M. L. Good, M. L. Stevenson, and H. K. Ticho, *Phys. Rev. Letters*, **2**, 114 (1959).

CHAPTER 5

Formalism

5.1. Addition and Resolution of Angular Momentum Vectors

Consider two angular momentum states $\left|j_1 m_1\right\rangle$ and $\left|j_2 m_2\right\rangle$ where j_i represents the angular momentum and m_i the component in a direction of quantization. These might represent the spin wave function of two particles or the spin wave function and spherical harmonic representing the orbital angular momentum of one particle. It is often desirable to consider a representation $\left|JM\right\rangle$ in terms of total angular momentum, J and its component M in a given direction. Conservation laws require that $M = m_1 + m_2$, and that only values of J such that $(j_1 + j_2) \geqslant J \geqslant \left|j_1 - j_2\right|$, subject to $J \geqslant \left|M\right|$, are admissible. We can then write:

$$\left|j_1 m_1\right\rangle \left|j_2 m_2\right\rangle = \sum_J \left\langle j_1 j_2 m_1 m_2 \middle| j_1 j_2 J M \right\rangle \left|JM\right\rangle$$

These expansion coefficients, vector addition coefficients, or Clebsch-Gordan coefficients, are the real matrix elements of a unitary orthogonal transformation. We have then the relations

$$\sum_{m_1} \sum_{m_2} \left\langle j_1 j_2 m_1 m_2 \middle| j_1 j_2 J_1 M_1 \right\rangle \left\langle j_1 j_2 m_1 m_2 \middle| j_1 j_2 J_2 M_2 \right\rangle = \delta_{J_1 J_2} \delta_{M_1 M_2}, \quad (1)$$

and

$$\sum_J \sum_M \left\langle j_1 j_2 m_1 m_2 \middle| j_1 j_2 J M \right\rangle \left\langle j_1 j_2 m_1' m_2' \middle| j_1 j_2 J M \right\rangle = \delta_{m_1 m_1'} \delta_{m_2 m_2'}$$

Furthermore, an angular momentum state can be resolved into two angular momentum states:

$$\left|JM\right\rangle = \sum_{j_1} \sum_{m_1} \left\langle j_1 j_2 m_1 m_2 \middle| j_1 j_2 J M \right\rangle \left|j_1 m_1\right\rangle \left|j_2 m_2\right\rangle \quad (2)$$

There is an arbitrary phase in the definition of the coefficients which must, however, be chosen consistently with the definition of the spherical harmonics. The convention of Condon and Shortley[1] is used here: Table 5-1 is a short table of Clebsch-Gordan coefficients, Table 5-2 a short table of spherical harmonics.

5.2. Scattering Formalism

Consider a flux of particles a, traveling in the z-direction incident upon a particle b. The wave function for this system can be written: $\psi = ab \exp (ikz)$, where a and b represent wave functions of the particles normalized over a unit volume and exp (ikz) is the plane wave function representing their respective motions: $k = p/\hbar$, where p is the center of mass momentum. Since $|\psi|^2 =$ one particle per unit volume, the flux is numerically equal to v, the velocity in the center of mass system.

The plane wave, exp (ikz), contains the sum of all angular momenta about any point. Choosing a description in spherical coordinates about any point of interaction, we have then: exp $(ikz) = \exp (ikr \cos \theta)$, which expanded in spherical harmonics is equal to $\sum_l A_l(kr) Y_l^0 (\theta,\phi)$. Only the spherical harmonics with $m = 0$ appear since there is no azimuthal dependence in the plane wave. The Y_l^0 are eigenfunctions of the angular momentum operator, and each quantity in the sum is then considered to be the partial wave corresponding to the orbital angular momentum, l, with z-component of orbital angular momentum equal to 0, in accord with the classical result and the corrspondence principle.

The radial part of the partial wave expansion $A_l (kr)$ can be evaluated from the relation: exp $(ikr \cos \theta) = \sum_l A_l (kr) Y_l^0 (\theta,\phi)$. Using the orthonormality of the spherical harmonics, we have: $A_l(kr) = \int \exp (ikr \cos \theta) Y_l^{0*} d\Omega$, and explicitly: $A_l(kr) = (4\pi)^{1/2} (2l + 1)^{1/2} i^l j_l (kr)$, where $j_l (kr)$ is equal to $(\pi/2kr)^{1/2} J_{l+1/2} (kr)$: where $J_{l+1/2} (kr)$ is a spherical Bessel function.

As $kr \to \infty$, the asymptotic form of $j_l(kr)$ is: $[\exp (i(kr - l\pi/2)) - \exp (-i(kr - l\pi/2))]/2ikr$ which represents the radial part of an incoming and outgoing spherical wave about the inter-

Table 5-1

Short Table of Clebsch-Gordan Coefficients[a]

$j_1 = 1/2, j_2 = 1/2, J = 1$

m_1		$1/2$	$-1/2$
m_2	$1/2$	1	$1/2$
	$-1/2$	$1/2$	1

$j_1 = 1, j_2 = 1/2, J = 3/2$

m_1		1	0	-1
m_2	$1/2$	1	$2/3$	$1/3$
	$-1/2$	$1/3$	$2/3$	1

$j_1 = 3/2, j_2 = 1/2, J = 2$

m_1		$3/2$	$1/2$	$-1/2$	$-3/2$
m_2	$1/2$	1	$3/4$	$1/2$	$1/4$
	$-1/2$	$1/4$	$1/2$	$3/4$	1

$j_1 = 2, j_2 = 1/2, J = 5/2$

m_1		2	1	0	-1	-2
m_2	$1/2$	1	$4/5$	$3/5$	$2/5$	$1/5$
	$-1/2$	$1/5$	$2/5$	$3/5$	$4/5$	1

$j_1 = 3/2, j_2 = 1, J = 1/2$

m_1		$3/2$	$1/2$	$-1/2$	$-3/2$
m_2	1			$1/6$	$1/2$
	0		$1/3$	$1/3$	
	-1	$1/2$	$1/6$		

$j_1 = 1, j_2 = 1/2, J = 1/2$

m_1		1	0	-1
m_2	$1/2$		$1/3$	$2/3$
	$-1/2$	$2/3$	$1/3$	

$j_1 = 3/2, j_2 = 1/2, J = 1$

m_1		$3/2$	$1/2$	$-1/2$	$-3/2$
m_2	$1/2$		$1/4$	$1/2$	$3/4$
	$-1/2$	$3/4$	$1/2$	$1/4$	

$j_1 = 2, j_2 = 1/2, J = 3/2$

m_1		2	1	0	-1	-2
m_2	$1/2$		$1/5$	$2/5$	$3/5$	$4/5$
	$-1/2$	$4/5$	$3/5$	$2/5$	$1/5$	

$j_1 = 1, j_2 = 1, J = 1$

m_1		1	0	-1
m_2	1		$1/2$	$1/2$
	0	$1/2$	0	$1/2$
	-1	$1/2$	$1/2$	

$j_1 = 3/2, j_2 = 1, J = 3/2$

m_1		$3/2$	$1/2$	$-1/2$	$-3/2$
m_2	1		$2/5$	$8/15$	$2/5$
	0	$3/5$	$1/15$	$1/15$	$3/5$
	-1	$2/5$	$8/15$	$2/5$	

$j_1 = 2, j_2 = 1, J = 1$					
m_1	2	1	0	-1	-2
m_2 1			1/10	3/10	3/5
m_2 0		3/10	2/5	3/10	
m_2 -1	3/5	3/10	1/10		

$j_1 = 2, j_2 = 1, J = 2$					
m_1	2	1	0	-1	-2
m_2 1		1/3	1/2	1/2	1/3
m_2 0	2/3	1/6	0	1/6	2/3
m_2 -1	1/3	1/2	1/2	1/3	

[a] $C = \langle j_1 j_2 m_1 m_2 | j_1 j_2 JM \rangle$, C^2 is tabulated; underscored values correspond to negative values of C. If $j_2 = 0$, $C = 1$; for $j_1 = j_2$, $J = 0$; $C = (-1)^{j_2 + m_2}/(2j_2 + 1)^{1/2}$

action center. At the interaction center, the outgoing wave will be changed by the interaction; the intensity may be reduced and the phase may be changed. This is represented by multiplying the outgoing wave by a complex number S_l, where $|S_l|^2 \leqslant 1$. Since the scattered wave is the difference between an undisturbed wave with $S = 1$, and the actual wave with asymptotic form

$$(2l + 1)^{1/2}(\pi^{1/2}/kr)i^{l+1}$$

$$[\exp{(i(kr - l\pi/2))} - S_l \exp{(-i(kr - l\pi/2))}]$$

the radial part of the partial scattered wave is

$$(A_l)_{\text{Sc.}} = (2l + 1)^{1/2}(\pi^{1/2}/kr)i^{l+1}(1 - S_l) \exp{(i(kr - l\pi/2))}$$

and the total scattered wave is

$$\psi_{\text{Sc.}} = \sum_l (A_l)_{\text{Sc.}} Y_l^0(\theta,\phi)$$

It is appropriate to emphasize here that the scattered wave, in the context in which it is used in this section, represents only the wave coherent with the incoming wave. Particles which have their energy, charge (as in charge exchange), or z-component of angular momentum changed are considered, in this sense, absorbed. Extensions to consider charge exchange and spin flip are discussed in Section 5.3. Since experimental procedures do not, as a practical matter, differentiate between elastic spin flip and nonspin flip scattering where spin flip refers to change in

Table 5-2

Spherical Harmonic Functions

Symbol	Function
$Y_0{}^0$	$\sqrt{(1/4\pi)}$
$Y_1{}^0$	$[\sqrt{(3/4\pi)}] \cos\theta$
$Y_1{}^1$	$-[\sqrt{(3/8\pi)}] \sin\theta\, e^{i\phi}$
$Y_1{}^{-1}$	$[\sqrt{(3/8\pi)}] \sin\theta\, e^{-i\phi}$
$Y_2{}^0$	$1/4[\sqrt{(5/\pi)}]\ (3\cos^2\theta - 1)$
$Y_2{}^1$	$-[\sqrt{(15/8\pi)}] \cos\theta \sin\theta\, e^{i\phi}$
$Y_2{}^{-1}$	$[\sqrt{(15/8\pi)}] \cos\theta \sin\theta\, e^{-1\phi}$
$Y_2{}^2$	$1/4[\sqrt{(15/2\pi)}]\ (1 - \cos^2\theta)\, e^{2i\phi}$
$Y_2{}^{-2}$	$1/4[\sqrt{(15/2\pi)}]\ (1 - \cos^2\theta)\, e^{-2i\phi}$

the z-component of the spin, the discussion of this section can be related directly to experiment only for the interaction of spinless particles.

With these restrictions, the differential scattering cross section in the direction θ, ϕ will be the asymptotic scattering intensity through a unit solid angle, $|\psi_{Sc.}|^2 \cdot r_0{}^2 d\Omega v$, divided by the incident flux, v, or $d\sigma/d\Omega = |\pi^{1/2}k^{-1}\sum_l(2l+1)^{1/2}(1-S_l)Y_l{}^0$ $(\theta,\phi)|^2$. The total scattering cross section, found by integration over the sphere, simplified by the orthonormality of the spherical harmonics, is

$$\sigma_{Sc.} = (\pi/k^2) \sum_l (2l+1)|1-S_l|^2 \tag{3}$$

The absorption cross section for a given partial wave is equal to the incoming current calculated from the incoming part of the wave minus the outgoing current, all divided by the incident flux, or

$$\sigma_{Ab.} = (\pi/k^2) \sum_l (2l+1)\ (1-|S_l|^2) \tag{4}$$

and the total cross section is the sum of the scattering and absorption cross sections

$$\sigma_t = (\pi/k^2) \sum_l (2l+1)\cdot 2(1-\mathrm{Re}S_l) \tag{5}$$

It is illuminating to consider the relation between the various cross sections, for a given partial wave, graphically. Consider the dimensionless scattering amplitude $A = i(1 - S)$ where $S = \eta \exp(2i\delta)$, where η the absorption factor, and δ the phase shift are real numbers such that $\eta \leqslant 1$. The scattering amplitude is then a vector on Figure 5-1, and the areas multiplied by $(2l + 1)\pi/k^2$ are equal to the respective cross sections.

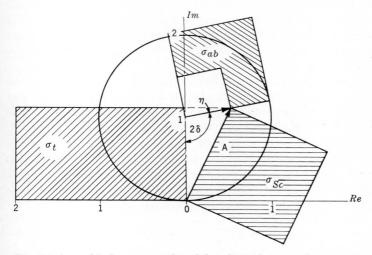

Fig. 5-1. A graphical representation of the relation between the scattering, absorption, and total cross sections for a given partial wave. Complex amplitudes are shown as vectors and cross sections as areas on the complex plane.

5.3. Scattering of Particles with Spin and Isotopic Spin

It is often necessary to examine the interaction of two particles, a and b, each of which is described in terms of symmetry properties, by quantum numbers which may represent spin and the component of spin in the beam direction, isotopic spin and the third component of isotopic spin, as well as strangeness, parity, and baryon number. Usually the interaction is invariant with respect to certain symmetry operations, such as rotation in space, and for the "strong interactions," rotation in isotopic spin space. Such symmetries as are represented by total angular momentum and total isotopic spin are then constants of motion, unchanged by the interaction. In order to exploit the constraints and relationships imposed by these conservation laws, it is desirable to construct from the spin of particles a and b and their orbital angular momentum initial states of definite total spin, total angular momentum, and isotopic spin; consider the effects of interactions on these states, and then resolve the final states again into particles a and b with specific charges and spin directions.

Specifically, consider a flux of particles a^ν traveling in the z-direction incident upon a particle b^μ, where ν and μ represent the third components of the isotopic spins of the particles. The wave function for this system is written as: $\Psi = a^\nu b^\mu \exp(ikz)$, where a^ν and b^μ now represent the normalized wave functions of these states, and $\exp(ikz)$ is again the plane wave function representing their respective motions. Total isotopic spin functions are constructed from the isotopic spin parts of the wave functions of a and b such that, in isotopic spin space:

$$\psi = \sum_T \langle t_a t_b \nu\mu | t_a t_b T\rho \rangle\, I_T{}^\rho$$

where t is the isotopic spin of particles a and b, and T and ρ are the total isotopic spin and total third component: $I_T{}^\rho$ is the isotopic spin wave function. We then consider the scattering of these states of definite isotopic spin.

If the particles a and b are unpolarized, the incident plane wave will consist of equally weighted, incoherent amplitudes of all of the spin states of a and b. This can be represented by writing the wave function for a as $a = (2i + 1)^{-1/2} \sum_m \epsilon_m a^m$ where a^m represent the normalized wave functions of particle a with spin i and z-component of angular momentum m. The ϵ are orthonormal vectors, such that $\epsilon_f \epsilon_g = \delta_{fg}$, introduced to represent formally the incoherence. Similarly, $b = (2s + 1)^{-1/2}$

$\sum_n \epsilon_n' b^n$, and the spin part of the wave function Ψ will consist of a number of terms such as $\epsilon_m \epsilon_n' a^m b^n$. It is convenient to construct states X with definite total spin, S, and z-component, N, by combining the spins of a and b:

$$a^m b^n = \sum_S \langle ismn | isSN \rangle X_S{}^N \tag{6}$$

The space part of the wave function, exp (ikz), is expanded, as in Section 5.2, into partial waves, each corresponding to a different orbital angular momentum:

$$\exp (ikz) = \sum_l A_l(kr) Y_l{}^0(\theta, \phi) \tag{7}$$

Different states, U, of total angular momentum, J, and z-component M, are then constructed from total spin and orbital angular momentum:

$$X_S{}^N Y_l{}^0 = \sum_J \langle SlN0 | SlJM \rangle U_J{}^M \tag{8}$$

The plane wave then has the form

$$\Psi = \sum_{\alpha\beta} \epsilon_n \epsilon_m C_{\alpha\beta} I_T{}^\rho U_J{}^M A_l(kr) \tag{9}$$

where α represents the quantum numbers T, J, l, and S; and β represents m, n, ν, and μ. The initial wave function is then the sum of states or partial waves factored into states of definite angular momentum and isotopic spin and radial parts with quantum numbers α and β, weighted according to $C_{\alpha\beta}$, a number equal to $(2i + 1)^{-1/2} (2j + 1)^{-1/2}$ multiplied by the product of the three Clebsch-Gordan coefficients introduced to form states of total isotopic spin, total spin, and total angular momentum.

For each state, the scattering is calculated in essentially the same way as in Section 5.2. The total scattered wave is then

$$\Psi_{\text{Sc.}} = \sum_{\alpha\beta} \epsilon_n \epsilon_m C_{\alpha\beta} I_T{}^\rho U_J{}^M (\pi^{1/2}/k) (2l + 1)^{1/2} (1 - S_\alpha) \tag{10}$$

The scattering matrix element S is a function only of the quantum numbers α. Usually, however, one is not interested in the scattering of states of total isotopic spin, but of definite charge states. It is then necessary to resolve the final states, of definite isotopic spin, into states of definite charge as

$$I_{T}{}^{\rho} = \sum_{\nu} \langle t_a t_b \nu \mu | t_a t_b T \rho \rangle \, a^{\nu} b^{\mu} \tag{11}$$

If angular distributions of the scattering, polarizations, and spin correlations are important, it is desirable also to resolve the total angular momentum to states of definite spin direction, a^m, b^n, and orbital angular momentum and the z-component and m, in a similar fashion.

Orthogonalities of spin and angular momentum functions simplify discussions of total cross section, total scattering cross section, and total absorption cross sections. Intensities of states of different total isotopic spin are additive; that is,

$$\left| \sum_{\rho} (A_{T}{}^{\rho} + A_{\theta}{}^{\rho}) \right|^2 = \sum_{\rho} (|A_{T}{}^{\rho}|^2 + |A_{\theta}{}^{\rho}|^2) \text{ as } \sum_{\rho} A_{T}{}^{\rho} A_{\theta}{}^{\rho} = \delta_{\theta T} \tag{12}$$

where the A_T and A_θ represent amplitudes for states of different total isotopic spin θ and T. To show that this is true, resolve the isotopic spin parts of A_T and A_θ:

$$I_{T}{}^{\rho} = \sum_{\nu} \langle t_a t_b \nu \mu | t_a t_b T \rho \rangle \, a^{\nu} b^{\mu}$$

and $\tag{13}$

$$I_{\theta}{}^{\rho} = \sum_{\nu'} \langle t_a t_b \nu' \mu' | t_a t_b \theta \rho \rangle \, a^{\nu'} b^{\mu'}$$

Then from the orthonormal character of spin functions, $a^{\nu} a^{\nu'} = \delta_{\nu \nu'}$, and $b^{\mu} b^{\mu'} = \delta_{\mu \mu'}$, and the property of Clebsch-Gordan coefficients:

$$\sum_{M} \langle j j' m m' | j j' J M \rangle \langle j j' m m' | j j' J' M \rangle = \delta_{J J'}$$

we have

$$\sum_{\rho} I_{T}{}^{\rho} I_{\theta}{}^{\rho} = \delta_{T \theta} \qquad \text{Q.E.D.} \tag{14}$$

Identical reasoning leads to orthogonality of states of different total spin: $\sum_{m} X_{S}{}^{m} X_{S'}{}^{m} = \delta_{SS'}$. And the relation

$$\int \sum_M (U_J{}^M) \, (U_{J'}{}^M)^* \mathrm{d}\Omega \; = \; \delta_{JJ'} \tag{15}$$

is deduced in a similar fashion with the conditions $a^\nu a^{\nu'}$ replaced by

$$X_S{}^m X_S{}^n = \delta_{mn} \quad \text{and} \quad \int Y_l{}^m Y_{l'}{}^m \, \mathrm{d}\Omega = \delta_{ll'} \delta_{mm'} \tag{16}$$

where the integrations are over the whole sphere.

Using these relations, summing over the quantum numbers β, integrating over the sphere, and evaluating the statistical weights for angular momentum explicity, we have for the total scattering cross section (here charge exchange scattering and spin flip scattering are considered to be elastic scattering),

$$\sigma_{\mathrm{Sc.}} = \pi k^{-2} \sum_{J,TS} \frac{(2J+1)}{(2i+1)(2s+1)} \langle t_a l_b \nu \mu | t_a l_b T_\rho \rangle^2 \, (1 - S_\alpha)^2 \tag{17}$$

The absorption cross section and the total cross section have the same form, but, as in Section 5.2, the last bracket is replaced by $1 - |S_\alpha|^2$, and $2(1 - \mathrm{Re}\, S_\alpha)$, respectively.

The relationships of Figure 5-1 are again valid; the areas are now multiplied by π/k^2 times the augmented statistical factors.

For reasons associated with the singular character of mass zero particles, spin 1 photon states can be described in terms of two states, χ^1 and χ^{-1}, with total angular momentum in the beam direction of $+1$ and -1, corresponding to right-handed and left-handed circularly polarized light. States of dipole moment l are constructed as by the vector addition of the photon spin state and an orbital angular momentum, l, to form a state of total angular momentum l, $l \neq 0$:

$$\chi^\varepsilon Y_l{}^0 = \langle 1 l \varepsilon 0 | 1 l l \varepsilon \rangle \, Y_l{}^\varepsilon(\theta, \phi) \tag{18}$$

Inversely, a radiation state carrying total angular momentum l and z-component, m, can be resolved into states of definite angular dependence and photon-polarization using the vector spherical harmonics.[2]

$$X_J{}^M = \sum_\varepsilon \langle 1 J \varepsilon m | 1 J J M \rangle \, \chi^\varepsilon Y_J{}^m \tag{19}$$

where $M = \mathcal{E} + m$, and $\chi^{+1} = 2^{-1/2}\,(\underline{x} + i\underline{y})$, $\chi^0 = \underline{z}$, and $\chi^{-1} = 2^{-1/2}\,(\underline{x} + i\underline{y})$, where $\underline{x}$, $\underline{y}$ and $\underline{z}$ are unit vectors representing polarization directions of the electromagnetic field. The angular distributions for electric dipole and magnetic dipole transitions are the same. However, the vectors $\underline{x}$, $\underline{y}$, and $\underline{z}$ represent electric field vectors or magnetic field vectors depending upon whether the transition is an M1, E2, $\cdots$ or an E1, M2, $\cdots$ transition, since the magnetic field is even and the electric field odd under space inversion, P.

5.4. Optical Theorem

An important theorem relates total cross sections to the imaginary part of a scattering amplitude. We will first ignore spin and isotopic spin states. Then $\sigma_{\text{tot}} = (\pi/k^2) \sum_l (2l + 1) \cdot 2 (1 - \text{Re } S_l)$.

The forward scattering amplitude for one partial wave l is

$$A_l(0) = \pi^{1/2}\,k^{-1}\,(2l + 1)^{1/2}\,i(1 - S_l)\,Y_l{}^0(0)$$

but $Y_l{}^0(0) = \{(2l + 1)/4\pi\}^{1/2}$

$$\text{and } ImA_l(0) = (1 - \text{Re } S_l) \cdot (2l + 1)/2k$$

Since amplitudes are additive,

$$ImA(0) = \sum_l ImA_l(0) \text{ and } \sigma_{\text{tot}} = 4\pi k^{-1}\,ImA(0) \qquad (20)$$

The interaction will, in general, be dependent upon the total spin. Since states of different total spin are incoherent, interactions of such states can be considered very much as interactions of different particles and the optical theorem will hold separately for each spin state weighted by the factor $(2S + 1)(2i + 1)^{-1}\,(2s + 1)^{-1}$ (see 5.3).

It is permissible, however, to disregard changes in spin direction; that is, one may consider spin flip as an absorption incoherent with the incoming beam, because spin flip terms do not contribute to the scattering pertinent to this theorem, the amplitude in the forward direction. The amplitude for states in which the z-component of the spin changes by $m\hbar$ is, by conservation of the z-component of angular momentum, proportional to Y_l^{-m}, which, for $m \neq 0$, vanishes at $\theta = 0$. Since the charge of the scattered particles is easily measured, change in the third component of isotopic spin of particles scattered in the forward direction is easily excluded, and isotopic spins may be ignored.

Since $d\sigma/d\Omega(0) = (\pi/k^2) \sum_S (2S + 1)$

$$(2i + 1)^{-1} (2s + 1)^{-1}|A_S(0)|^2 \tag{21}$$

lower limits may often be placed on the value of the scattering cross section in the forward direction. This is particularly useful in the interpretation of the interactions of spin 0 or spin 1/2 particles; with spin 0 particles $d\sigma/d\Omega \geqslant |ImA(0)|^2 \geqslant k^2\sigma_t^2/4\pi$. Note that at high energies, for a constant total cross section, the differential cross section in the forward direction will have a lower bound which will vary as E^2.

5.5. Angular Momentum Barriers

Classically, a particle with momentum p cannot interact with or be emitted from a region of radius a with an angular momentum greater than pa. However, the uncertainty principle suggests that the classical constraints will break down in the region of small quantum numbers. There will be an uncertainty in θ, the angle of scattering or emission of a particle, of the order of $\Delta\theta = 1/l$ where l is the angular momentum; and $\Delta\theta$ will be equal to $\Delta p/p$, where Δp is transverse to the direction of motion. Since $\Delta p \cdot \Delta a \approx \hbar$, the particle position will not be defined within a value $\Delta a \approx \hbar l/p$, and there will be some probability of finding particles with angular momentum $(\hbar l) > (pa)$ in the interaction region. Such particles can be considered to pass through a region in which their kinetic energy, $T(r) = T(\infty) - (l/r)^2/(2m)$, is negative. In analogy with the effects of a repulsive coulomb field, the reduction of probability of interaction of a particle of high angular momentum is considered as an effect of a centrifugal

barrier, and the magnitude of that reduction is considered a
barrier penetration factor.

Though for any sufficiently well-defined problem, the consequences of the angular momentum barrier are an implicit
part of a complete solution, for short-range interactions the
specific effect of angular momentum is often obscure. For short-
range interactions, the effects of angular momentum are seldom
strongly energy dependent inside the interaction region, but
are often explicitly calculable and strongly energy dependent
outside that region. It is then often practical and desirable to
make the approximation that the problem can be divided into
internal and external parts, and consider explicit calculations or
better, estimates, concerning the centrifugal barrier. There is no
universal barrier penetration factor: the form and use of such
factors depend on the problem in question.

Though these considerations are justified by more sophisticated calculations, it is convenient to discuss the effects of
centrifugal barriers on nonresonant scattering and reaction cross
sections using perturbation theory.

Scattering and reaction cross sections can be defined as the
number of interactions per scattering center divided by the unit
incident flux: this is just equal to $v_i^{-1}(2\pi/\hbar) \langle \psi_f | H | \psi_i \rangle^2 dN_f/dE$,
where v_i is the center of mass velocity of the incident state and
dN_f/dE is the density of final states, proportional to v_f. The
matrix element between initial and final plane wave states can
be expected to be proportional to the amplitude of these states
at an interaction radius R, the boundary of the interaction
region, and is then proportional to $(j_l(k_f R))^2 \cdot (j_n(k_i R)^2$, where n
and l are the respective orbital angular momenta for
incident and final states. For elastic scattering, $l = n$, $k_i = k_f$,
and we have $(\sigma_e)_l \simeq (j_l(kR))^2 \cdot (j_l(kR))^2$. For $kR \ll 1$, $j_l(kR) \to$
$(kR)^l/(2l + 1)!!$ and $(\sigma_e)_l \approx [(kR)^l/(2l + 1)!!]^4$. Since for elastic
scattering $(\sigma_e)_l \approx k^{-2} \sin^2 \delta_l$, for $kR \to 0$, $\delta_l = k^{2l+1}$. Near the
threshold for a new channel, where $k_f R \ll 1$, and the variation
with energy of the initial state can be neglected, we have
$(\sigma_f)_l \approx (j_l(k_f R))^2 k_f R \approx (kR)^{2l+1}/[(2l + 1)!!]^2$. This can be con-

sidered as the basic penetration factor; for scattering, this factor is applied both to incoming and outgoing flux.

There are obvious limitations to the above considerations. While the threshold relations are rigidly valid, at least for a sufficiently small energy interval, it is clearly possible to construct a potential such that for any particular angular momentum and energy the scattering phase shift is $90°$; the cross section is then $(2l + 1) \, 4\pi \, k^{-2}$ multiplied by spin statistical factors, and is then determined only by conservation laws, and is seemingly independent of penetration factors. For values of $kR > l$, such a situation can arise only as the result of a resonance or the formation of an excited state, and it is simplest to consider the effects of the penetration barrier as an effect on the lifetime of the state. This lifetime will be equal to some natural time determined by the internal wave function multiplied by a penetration factor representing the ratio of the intensity of the wave function at ∞, to the intensity at an interaction radius R. Consider the incoming wave with an asymptotic form for the radial part of $r\psi$ as $U_l(r) \, e^{-ikr}$, $r \to \infty$. At R, the amplitude has the form $U_l(R) = (-1)^l j_{-l-1} \, (kR) - i j_l \, (kR)$. For $kR \ll 1$, the ratio $[U_l(kR)/U_l(\infty)]^2$ is again $[(kR)^l/(2l + 1)!!]^2$. The lifetime τ is lengthened by the inverse of this factor, and the width of the resonance $\Gamma = \hbar/\tau$ is then reduced by this factor.

This previous discussion, which suggests relations between cross section and transition probabilities for different values of l, implicitly assumes an interaction very like a square well. Since the intensity of the high angular momentum part of the plane wave falls off very rapidly for small values of R, the important part of their interaction must derive from the tail of the potential; a tail whose relative importance is reduced by a treatment involving a definite fictitious interaction radius R. Indeed it can be shown that the "long-tailed" Yukawa potential, expected to be relevant for many fundamental particle reactions, at large distances contributes relatively more to high angular momentum. It is convenient to discuss this explicitly by the use of the mechanics of dispersion theory. To be definite, we consider the scattering of two spinless particles dominated by the exchange of a virtual particle of mass m. The scattering amplitude, expressed as a function of $x = \cos\theta$, will have a pole at $x_0 = 1 + (mc/2p)^2$, and will then be proportional to $1/(x_0 - x)$, which expanded in spherical harmonics is equal to $(4\pi)^{1/2}\sum_l Q_l(x_0) Y_l^0(x)$, where the $Q_l(x_0)$ are the Legendre functions of the second kind. The partial cross section for angular momentum l is then $4\pi Q_l^2(x_0)$; asymptotically as $k\hbar/mc = ka \to 0$, $x_0 \to 1/2 (ka)^{-2}$, $Q_l(x_0) \to (\pi/l)^{1/2}(2x_0)^{-l-1}$ and $4\pi Q_l^2(x_0) \to (4\pi^2/l)(ka)^{4l-4}$. Dividing through by the partial cross section for $l = 0$, as a normalization, we have $(\sigma_e)_l \approx (1/l)(ka)^{4l}$, where again the basic penetration factor, proportional to $(ka)^{2l}$ comes in twice for scattering. This penetration factor is larger than that from the previous calculation by a factor, $l^{-1/2}[(2l + 1)!!]^2$; hence, partial waves of high angular momentum play a much more important part than is implied by the introduction of a discrete boundary.[3]

5.6. Scattering Matrix

In Section 5.2, the wave function representing the scattered wave was normalized to correspond to an incident flux v — a choice which simplified the determination of cross sections. The expansion into waves of definite orbital angular momentum resulted in an expression which represented asymptotically, for each partial wave, incoming and outgoing spherical waves. If a different normalization is chosen, a normalization such that the incoming flux for each partial wave is unitary, the scattered wave has the form

$$\psi_{aa} = \frac{\exp\left(-i(k_a r_a - l_a\pi/2)\right) - S_{aa}\exp\left(i(k_a r_a - l_a\pi/2)\right)}{(4\pi v_a)^{1/2} r_a} \quad (22)$$

The subscript, a, represents the channel or pair of reaction products. In general, there will be more than one channel, other pairs of particles b, c, etc., will be produced by the interaction of particles a. To represent these, we add to Equation 22, equations such as:

$$\psi_{ab} = -S_{ab} \exp\left(i(k_b r_b - l_b \pi/2)\right)/[(4\pi v_b)^{1/2} \, r_b] \qquad (23)$$

and

$$\Psi_a = \sum_b \psi_{ab}$$

The intensity of each outgoing wave is $|S_{ab}|^2$.

For the initial pair of particles a, N complex constants $S_{aa}, S_{ab}, S_{ac}, \cdots$, are necessary to describe the asymptotic behavior of the wave function, if N different channels are available. Since any one of the channels may be the initial channel, there are a total of N^2 constants to describe the interactions of all pairs of particles. These can be considered as an $N \times N$ matrix—the scattering matrix.

The scattering matrix is important inasmuch as it allows a compact description of the properties of asymptotic wave functions; relationships which are independent of the details of the interactions. These essential properties of the scattering matrix are not changed by the increased complexity required to consider the spins of particles and states of three or more particles and these generalizations will not be discussed.

The unitary character of the scattering matrix is established using a lemma; the scalar product of two solutions of the wave equation is time independent.

$$\partial/\partial t \langle u|v \rangle = \langle \partial u/\partial t|v \rangle + \langle u|\partial v/\partial t \rangle$$
$$= i/\hbar \left(\langle Hu|v \rangle - \langle u|Hv \rangle \right) = 0 \qquad (24)$$

Before the interaction, $\langle \psi_a|\psi_b \rangle = \delta_{ab}$, as the incoming waves are normalized to unit intensity and waves in different channels cannot interfere. Extending these relations to describe the situation after collision, we have, simply, $\sum_k S^*_{ka} \, S_{kb} = \delta_{ab}$. In matrix notation $S^\dagger S = 1$; the formal expression that the S-matrix is unitary. Conservation of probability is contained in the subsidiary relation $\sum_k |S_{ak}|^2 = 1$.

Cross sections can be written in terms of the S-matrix elements simply by using for the flux in the incoming channel the flux from the expansion of the plane wave; exp (ikz). Then from Section 5.2, the cross section for the process $a \rightarrow b$ is

$$\sigma_{ab} = (2l + 1)\pi k^{-2}|\delta_{ab} - S_{ab}|^2$$

Invariance under time reversal establishes further relations among the S-matrix elements. Generally, the time reversal operator takes the form of a transformation by a unitary operator, U, plus complex conjugation, and the condition for invariance of the Hamiltonian under time reversal is $H^* = U^{-1} H U$. Consider the wave function ψ which obeys the equation $H\psi = i\hbar(\partial\psi/\partial t)$; under complex conjugation, $H^*\psi^* = i\hbar [\partial\psi^*/\partial(-t)]$, then $U^{-1} HU \psi^* = i\hbar[\partial\psi^*/\partial(-t)]$, and $HU \psi^* = i\hbar[\partial U\psi^*/\partial(-t)]$. The function $U\psi^*$ is then the time reversed solution—a solution developing backwards in time. Typically, the complex conjugation has the result of reversing the momenta and the operator U is a spin reversal operator such as σ_y.

Neglecting spins, the time reversed wave function corresponding to Ψ_a is Ψ_a^*, which now represents a situation in which there are many incoming waves and only one outgoing wave. This time reversed wave function Ψ_a^* can then be expanded as a sum of of non-time-reversed functions: $\Psi_a^* = \sum_b C_b \Psi_b$. Before the reaction takes place, only one channel is open for each of the Ψ_b; comparing both sides of the equation then, C_b must be equal to $-S_{ab}^*$. After the reaction takes place, there is only one channel open for Ψ_a^*, and again comparing both sides of the equation, $\sum_\gamma S_{a\gamma}^* S_{\gamma b} = \delta_{ab}$, or in matrix notation, $S^*S = 1$. Then, $S^*S = S^\dagger S; S^* = S^\dagger, S_{ab}^* = S_{ba}^*$, and $S_{ab} = S_{ba}$, which is the reciprocity theorem.[4]

5.7. Watson's Theorem

Consider a reaction involving only two channels a and b, where the interaction in channel a is very weak: $|\delta_{a\gamma} - S_{a\gamma}| \ll 1$. The S-matrix

$$\begin{vmatrix} S_{aa} & S_{ab} \\ S_{ba} & S_{bb} \end{vmatrix} \approx \begin{vmatrix} 1 & S_{ab} \\ S_{ba} & \exp(2i\delta) \end{vmatrix}$$

where δ is the scattering phase shift in channel b. Since $SS^* = 1$ from invariance under time reversal $(SS^*)_{21} = S_{ba} + S^*_{ba} \cdot \exp(2i\delta) = 0$, and $S_{ab} = |S_{ab}| \exp(\delta - \pi/2)$. Since only the relative phases of final states are important, the factor of $-\pi/2$ can be dropped, and the phases of the final state amplitudes are just the scattering phase shifts pertinent to that channel. This result, first derived by Watson,[5] is particularly pertinent in the study of photoproduction and the weak decays of elementary particles. For the weak decays, S_{aa} can be considered equal to 1, and S_{ab} then represents the matrix element for decay. Though these results concerning final state phases are valid if many weak channels are open, no simple and general relations hold if more than one strongly interacting channel is important; that is, if $|S_{bb}|^2$ is not very nearly equal to 1. If a channel c is important, the element of the matrix product $(SS^*)_{21} = 0$ has the explicit form: $S_{ab} + S_{ba}^* S_{bb} + S_{bc} S_{ca}^*$ and the general properties of the S-matrix do not require a simple relation for the phase of S_{ab}. Though, near threshold, S_{ab}, S_{ba}^*, and S_{bc} are all proportional to $k^{(2l+1)/2}$, where l is the orbital angular momentum in channel b; the amplitudes for different partial waves are not even required to be relatively real at threshold.

5.8. Anomalies at Threshold

From the considerations of Section 5.5, we note that just above threshold the amplitude representing the S-wave production of the two particles will vary as $k^{1/2}s$, and the cross section as $k|s|^2$, where s is a complex number, essentially independent of energy, given here the dimensions of $(\text{length})^{1/2}$, and k is the wave number representing the center of mass momentum in that channel. From the unitary character of the S-matrix, we can expect that this sharp increase in a partial cross section will be reflected in the cross sections for other processes. Consider the behavior of the production amplitude for the reaction $A + B \rightarrow C + D$ near the threshold for the process $A + B \rightarrow E + F$. We denote the channels (A, B), (C, D), and (E, F) as α, β, and γ, respectively, and consider an expansion of the S-matrix about threshold for channel γ in powers of $k^{1/2}$ where k is the center of mass wave number of the γ channel. The change in S can be expressed as a unitary transformation[6]: $S = US_T U^{-1}$, where $U = \exp{(ik^{1/2} A)}$; S_T is the S-matrix at threshold. The k is the center of mass wave number of channel γ, and A is a real Hermitian matrix. Expanding, $U = I + ik^{1/2} A - kA^2/2 \cdots$, where I is the unit matrix. Then $S = US_T U^{-1} = S_T + ik^{1/2} B + (1/2)kC \cdots$, where B, for example, is equal to $(AS_T - S_TA)$. Writing out $SS^\dagger = S_TS_T{}^\dagger + ik^{1/2}\alpha + k\beta \cdots$, and noting that $SS^\dagger$ and $S_TS_T{}^\dagger$ must both be equal to 1 as S and S_T are unitary, the momentum dependent terms must vanish and $\alpha = \beta = 0$. This is true if $C = BS_T{}^\dagger B$. We write explicitly:

$$S_T = \begin{vmatrix} S_{\alpha\alpha} & S_{\alpha\beta} & 0 \\ S_{\alpha\beta} & S_{\beta\beta} & 0 \\ 0 & 0 & 1 \end{vmatrix} \quad \text{and } B = \begin{vmatrix} 0 & 0 & s_{\beta\gamma} \\ 0 & 0 & s_{\alpha\gamma} \\ s_{\gamma\alpha} & s_{\gamma\beta} & 0 \end{vmatrix}$$

where the s are energy independent. This form of B is set by the physical arguments of Section 5.3. Performing the multiplication $BS^\dagger{}_T B$ we have for the matrix element $S_{\alpha\beta} = (S_{\alpha\beta})_T + (1/2)ks_{\alpha\gamma}s_{\gamma\beta}$. Below threshold, the channel γ will be closed and the S-matrix will have one less row and column, but elements such as $S_{\alpha\beta}$ are analytically continuable below threshold where k becomes imaginary. The wave function in channel γ will have the form $e^{ikz/r}$ above threshold, and be damped exponentially as $e^{-\kappa z/r}$ below threshold. So $k \rightarrow i\kappa$, where κ is positive. When plotted as an increasing function of energy, the loci of the dimensionless scattering amplitude $S_{\alpha\beta}$, plotted on the complex plane, makes a left turn of $90°$ at the γ threshold, and the reaction cross section, $\sigma_{\alpha\beta}$, proportional to $\pi k_\alpha{}^{-2}|S_{\alpha\beta}|^2$, has the form $a(E - E_t)^{1/2}$ above threshold and $b(E_t - E)^{1/2}$ below threshold, where a and b are constants determined by the values of the elements of S_T and

B. If *a* and *b* are both negative, the cross section $\sigma_{\alpha\beta}$ will reach a cusplike maximum at the threshold for channel γ. If one of the two particles of channel γ is unstable and decays with an appreciable width, the sharp cusp will be smoothed out and look very like a resonance.[7]

REFERENCES

1. E. U. Condon and G. H. Shortley, *Theory of Atomic Spectra*, Cambridge University Press, London, 1935.
2. J. M. Blatt and V. F. Weisskopf, *Theoretical Nuclear Physics*, Wiley, New York, 1952.
3. This view was suggested to us by R. Dalitz.
4. This section follows closely the treatments of J. M. Blatt and V. F. Weisskopf, *ibid.*
5. K. M. Watson, *Phys. Rev.*, **95**, 228 (1954); M. Gell-Mann and K. M. Watson, *Ann. Rev. Nucl. Sci.*, **4**, 219 (1954).
6. E. P. Wigner, *Phys. Rev.*, **73**, 1002 (1948); G. Breit, *Phys. Rev.*, **107**, 1612 (1957); A. N. Baz and L. B. Okun, *Soviet Phys. JETP (English Transl.)*, **8**, 525 (1959).
7. M. Nauenberg and A. Pais, *Phys. Rev. Letters*, **8**, 82 (1962).

Author Index*

Italic numbers refer to the bibliographies of the different chapters.

Nauenberg, M., 79 (ref. 35), *90*, 137 (ref. 7), *137*
Newth, J. A., 2 (ref. 5), *13*
Nishijima, K., 5, 9, *14*, 16 (ref. 3), *36*
Noon, J., 2 (ref. 7), *14*
Nordin, P., Jr., 22 (ref. 9), 25 (ref. 15), *36*, *37*
Novey, T. B., 11 (ref. 25), *15*

Occhialini, G. P. S., 1 (ref. 1), 2 (ref. 4), *13*
O'Ceallaigh, C., 2 (ref. 7), *14*
Oehme, R., 32 (ref. 21), *37*, 41 (ref. 4), *88*
Okubo, S., 23 (ref. 12), *36*
Okun, L. B., 1 (ref. 1), *13*, 50 (ref. 9), *88*, 95 (ref. 6), *116*, 136 (ref. 6), *137*
Olbert, S., 2 (ref. 5), 3 (ref. 5e), *14*
Orear, J., 101 (ref. 13), 105 (ref. 13), *116*
Overseth, O. E., 111 (ref. 22), *117*

Page, D. I., 2 (ref. 5), *13*
Pais, A., 5, *14*, 32 (ref. 21), 35 (ref. 23), *37*, 41 (ref. 3), 79 (ref. 35), *88*, *90*, 112 (ref. 23), *117*, 137 (ref. 7), *137*
Pal, Y., 2 (ref. 7), *14*
Pancini, E., 5 (ref. 10), *14*
Panetti, M., 8 (ref. 18), *14*
Peierls, R. F., 79 (ref. 35), *90*
Perl, M., 25 (ref. 14), *37*, 108 (ref. 18), *116*
Peters, B., 2 (ref. 7), *14*
Peterson, J. R., 101 (ref. 15), *116*
Pevsner, A., 84 (ref. 43), *91*, 101 (ref. 15), 110 (ref. 20), *116*, *117*
Peyrou, C. H., 8 (ref. 20), *14*
Piccioni, O., 5 (ref. 10), *14*, 35 (ref. 23), 36 (ref. 25), *37*
Plano, R., 22 (ref. 7), 25 (ref. 14),

36, *37*, 47 (ref. 7), *88*, 108 (ref. 18), 115 (ref. 29), *116*, *117*
Pniewski, J., 80 (ref. 36), *90*
Pontecorvo, B., 95 (ref. 6), *116*
Powell, C. F., 2, *13*, *14*
Powell, W. M., 25 (ref. 15), 36 (ref. 25), *37*, 96 (ref. 7), 97 (ref. 9), 115 (ref. 9), *116*
Prentki, J., 17 (ref. 4), *36*
Prodell, A., 22 (ref. 7), 25 (ref. 14), *36*, *37*, 47 (ref. 7), *88*, 108 (ref. 18), 115 (ref. 29), *116*, *117*
Puppi, G., 22 (ref. 7), 25 (ref. 14), *36*, *37*, 47 (ref. 7), *88*, *93*, 108 (ref. 18), 110 (ref. 20), *116*, *117*

Rahm, D. C., 53 (ref. 14), *88*
Rau, R. R., 3 (ref. 8), *14*, 53 (ref. 14), *88*
Ravenhall, D. G., 67 (ref. 45), *91*
Rediker, R. H., 2 (ref. 5), 3 (ref. 5c), *13*
Reynolds, G. T., 3 (ref. 8), *14*
Rhee, Y. I., 94 (ref. 5), 98 (ref. 5), *116*
Ringo, G. R., 11 (ref. 25), *15*
Ritson, D. M., 2 (ref. 7), *14*, 50 (ref. 8), *88*, 101 (ref. 15), *116*
Robson, J., 11 (ref. 25), *15*
Rochester, G. D., 1, 2, *13*
Roe, B. P., 19 (ref. 2), *36*
Rosenfeld, A. H., 1 (ref. 1), *13*, 19 (ref. 1), 22 (ref. 9), 25 (ref. 15), *36*, *37*, 70 (ref. 28b), 77 (ref. 33), *90*, 94 (refs. 4, 5), 98 (ref. 5), 102 (ref. 16), 114 (ref. 27), *116*, *117*
Ross, R., 63 (ref. 23), 67 (ref. 45), *89*, *91*
Rossi, B., 2 (ref. 5), 3, *14*
Rossum, L., van, 50 (ref. 8), *88*
Rouhaninejad, H., 26 (ref. 17), *37*, 52 (ref. 11), *88*

Subject Index

147